Running
For
Your Life

Running For Your Life

EXPLORING THE AMAZING BENEFITS OF REGULAR EXERCISE

Rob Fryer

PALMETTO
PUBLISHING

Charleston, SC
www.PalmettoPublishing.com

Running For Your Life

www.robfryer.com

First Edition

Paperback ISBN: 979-8-8229-0275-6
eBook ISBN: 979-8-8229-0276-3

To my wife, Margie; my children, Ann and Stephen;
and in memory of my late parents, Tony and Mercia,
who showered their three children with
affection and encouragement.

Contents

Preface

As a runner, what I lack in achievements I make up for in longevity. As my running career nears the fifty-year mark, I have decided it is time to share some of my experiences, particularly what I have learned about the importance of exercise for our physical—and mental—well-being. Accordingly, this book is partly biographical to illustrate the joy I have gained from years of running—and still do. More importantly, it includes the knowledge I have accumulated regarding the amazing health benefits of regular exercise, whether running or another activity.

Part of this book, primarily the third chapter, presents a snapshot of published research confirming these benefits, including how exercise reduces the risk of developing cardiovascular disease, type 2 diabetes, and some cancers, which can mean additional years of good health—a longer health span—and potentially a longer life span. All of the studies I have seen, however, are in a sense "latitudinal," in that they included a number of volunteers, in some cases thousands, recruited at the time the study began. While a few studies followed participants for more than two decades, none followed them for anywhere near five decades. I see myself as a single "longitudinal" case study of the benefits of regular physical activity maintained for nearly fifty years of adult life; I have therefore included information on the distances I have run over the decades, as well as on my health and personal well-being. I am now seventy-six. I run most days and have reaped the payback from my ongoing commitment to being active every day. So can most of us.

If you are a runner, I hope you will learn a thing or two from my experiences. Most of all, I hope I can inspire you to run for the rest of your life. If you do not currently exercise on a regular basis and are thinking about it, my hope is you will learn enough about the health benefits of regular physical activity, whether running, walking, or something else, and become inspired to start. I wish you good health for many years to come.

Chapter 1

Patriots' Day, 2013

I made a left turn onto Boylston Street, the finish line straight ahead, some ten city blocks away. The crowds on the sidewalks were thinner than they would have been two hours earlier to witness the top runners finish, but they continued to cheer the rest of us enthusiastically. I imagine many were there waiting for a friend or family member to come by. My mind was tired, and my legs were weary on that mild April day, but the end of the race was near. Once I could read the digital clock above the finish line, I realized I still had a chance to finish in three hours, fifty-seven minutes, a revised goal I had set for myself as I neared downtown Boston, for a reason I shall explain in a moment.

I picked up the pace as best I could as I passed the twenty-six-mile marker and focused on the finish line straight ahead, now oblivious to the crowd noise. I planted my racing flats on the electronic carpet that records finish times in three hours, fifty-seven minutes, and fifty-eight seconds. I moved slowly through the long finish chute as I had done several times before in Boston dating back to 1992. I knew the drill well: bow so a volunteer could hang a medal around my neck, take a foil blanket and wrap it around myself to keep warm, take a banana or two to replace calories burned, take a bottle of water from another friendly volunteer who had probably been doing this for the last two hours, and finally reach a long line of yellow school buses. These buses had taken runners from the city to the start in Hopkinton and then brought their dry clothes and other possessions in labeled tog bags from there to the finish area.

1

The lines of buses seemed to stretch on forever on my left and right, displaying race numbers in ascending order on the windows. I slowly made my way along the rows for two city blocks until I made it to the bus on the left that would have the bag matching my race number. I reached a window around the middle of the bus that had a sign reading "18180 to 18200" for the twenty bags on the seat by that window. I showed my race number, 18188, pinned to my running top under the foil blanket, and yet another patient volunteer reached for my bag. As she handed it to me, there was a loud *thud* from the direction of the finish line a couple hundred yards away. Taking my bag with both hands, I looked to my left and saw smoke rising. Could this be a gas line explosion? Somehow the sound instantly reminded me of the only improvised device explosion I had heard before, at the back of the magistrates' court in Johannesburg, South Africa, in 1987. That explosion occurred during the apartheid struggles and had claimed several lives.

There were many runners and volunteers near where I was standing at that moment, but there was no sense of panic; no one knew what had happened. People just looked at one another. A few moments later, there was a second explosion from the same direction. It seemed further away and was not as loud. There was still no sense of panic, only bewilderment. Carrying my bag, I continued walking to the end of the line of buses and left the finish area. I found a quiet spot to pull on some warm clothes, took my mobile phone out of the bag, and turned it on, only to find there was no signal for some reason. I then headed for the nearby Arlington underground station by the Public Garden to take the Green Line T train to a station near the western suburb of Needham and my son's apartment.

At the station entrance, a policeman told me it was now closed. I asked him what had happened; either he did not know or would not say. I saw that roads in the area were rapidly being closed off. Now what? At least I had dry clothes on and was not cold. It was a fairly cool day for mid-April. As I later learned, the race was suspended, and of the 23,342 starters, over 5,600 runners behind me were unable to complete the race or get anywhere near the finish area to retrieve clothes, money, phones, keys, and so on.[1] I decided the best thing to do would be to leave the area on foot; perhaps if I continued walking in the same easterly direction, I would find a T station that was open or would at least be able to make a phone call to my son and daughter, who were together in Needham. They had watched the race awhile and cheered me on two hours earlier in the suburb of Wellesley, around the halfway mark. They might know what happened or how I might get to Needham.

Some distance beyond the Boston Common, I came upon an electronics store with a TV on in the window and a crowd around it. No one was speaking; everyone was stunned—the script on the bottom of the screen said a bomb (in fact two) had been detonated near the finish line of the 117th Boston Marathon a few minutes after I crossed the finish line. There was no information on casualties yet. A message flashed on the screen that said the Green Line T was completely shut down. I took out my phone. It had a signal. I later learned that cellular service had been shut down around the finish area in case phones were being used to detonate explosives. I called my two children to let them know I had finished the marathon and was OK and to ask them to call my wife in Connecticut. They were both working and did not have the TV on, so they knew nothing of what had happened. I asked them to check online whether suburban trains were running from Boston's South Station so I could get out of central Boston. They could not find any information to say they were not. I then asked someone the way to South Station; he said just keep walking in the same direction. And so I did.

It took me around half an hour to reach South Station. However, I had no grounds for complaint—I learned later innocent spectators had been killed and maimed on this tragic day. I had finished the race, received my medal, retrieved my dry clothes, and was safe and unharmed. Upon arrival at the station, I found that suburban trains were running normally, and I bought a ticket to Needham station, near my son's place. With it being the Patriots' Day holiday, the train was not crowded, however, a number of the passengers were marathon runners who may have had experiences similar to mine. The mood was somber—uncharacteristic for a bunch of runners who had just completed and earned a medal at the oldest marathon in the world bar the Olympics.

And so, this was the ending to my seventy-sixth race over the standard marathon distance of 42.195 kilometers or 26 miles 385 yards on April 15, 2013. It was also my 119th finish over the marathon distance or longer, including thirteen Comrades Marathons of around ninety kilometers or fifty-six miles—the world's oldest and largest ultramarathon, which I describe in chapter 12.

My running career began in 1974 in Johannesburg, South Africa, over a beer with a work colleague and neighbor, James, who encouraged me to join him on his daily fifteen-minute early-morning run at 6:00 a.m. It was winter in the southern hemisphere, so we ran every day in the dark. Three months after I started those daily runs, which by then included longer weekend runs, I was persuaded—stupidly, I would suggest—to run my first marathon. It was the twenty-seventh Jackie Gibson Memorial Marathon on August 18, 1974. The Jackie Gibson is the oldest marathon in Johannesburg, first run in 1946, and is still held every year. Unlike Boston, which is a point-to-point course, this was a circular course, through the hilly southern suburbs of the city, starting and finishing at a sports club. The halfway mark was around the lowest point of the course; every runner knows what that means—a grueling second half—and Johannesburg is at an altitude of more than 5,000 feet.

Jackie Gibson was a South African marathon runner and air force lieutenant who finished eighth in the 1936 Berlin Olympics at the age of twenty-two and tragically died in an aircraft accident in 1944 at the age of twenty-nine.

In those days, fields for marathons were small. Boston is reported to have had 1,398 finishers in 1974;[2] the Gibson had a fraction of that, around 250 by my estimation. Refreshment stations were nonexistent in Johannesburg back then. Therefore, the only way to receive drinks—and in a race of the marathon distance you have to drink regularly—was to have someone drive along the route ahead of you and hand drinks to you at suitable intervals. I was assisted in this way by a friend named John who had been running for a couple of years and who had completed a few marathons. I felt great for the first hour or so, enjoying the downhill running. John told me a few times I might be going too fast. He was right. Marathons are unforgiving if you are underprepared, and I was. The hills in the second half became a real struggle but seeing a friend at regular intervals with a drink and a generous dose of encouragement was of immense help, assistance that is rarely possible today. John's calculations of my expected finish time became more pessimistic every time we saw each other, and for the last ten kilometers, we were both focused on trying to finish under four hours, the time limit to receive a medal and qualify as an official finisher! Running was not for the fainthearted in those days.

Fortunately, the final stretch of road was relatively flat, and I was able to pick up the pace just a little and finish the course, with a lap of a sports field, in 3 hours, 57 minutes. I have no record of the seconds. I was overjoyed to complete my first marathon. I knew it would not be the last.

I ran my second marathon six months later in 3 hours, 27 minutes, much better prepared, and my third seven months after that in 3 hours, 6 minutes. I was on my way; never again would I come near 3 hours, 57 minutes, until Boston in 2013. From 1974 until 2004, I ran at least one marathon a year. Some years, I ran several of them. I finished in under three hours many times.

Ever since that August day in 1974, I had wanted Jackie Gibson, my first marathon, to be my slowest marathon. I clocked the same time on Boylston Street, at least to the nearest minute. In 2013, Boston had been a struggle—one of those days. As I sat in the train to Needham, Massachusetts, I asked myself, "Do I bookend my marathon career with two 3-hour-57-minute marathons, seventy-six finishes at the marathon distance over nearly forty years, and a day of drama in Boston with tragic consequences?" I am still not sure I know the answer. What was never a question in my mind, however, was that I would continue to run for my life.

CHAPTER 2

Why Do We Run?

W hy would I write this book and hope that you would read it? I am a fairly average, though quite hardworking, runner. In high school, a long time ago, I was a decent runner, though hardly a star, competing in the sprints and long jump. I could also beat about half the field in cross-country races, but I was pretty hopeless at middle-distance track events like the 800 and 1,500 meters—the events where future long-distance stars are often successful in their youth.

That was back in the early 1960s. DNA analysis has revealed, not surprisingly, that I have predominantly fast-twitch muscle fibers, as is typical of sprinters.[3] Over the years I have developed reasonable lung capacity, as measured by VO_2 max, but it's nothing special. VO_2 max is a measure of the body's ability to transport and use oxygen while exercising—a test of cardiovascular fitness. In my best years, I managed just under 38 minutes a couple of times over the 10k distance on the road, and my best marathon time is 2 hours and 44 minutes, at altitude in Johannesburg, South Africa. These times were probably close to my potential as a recreational runner. I am certainly not a star athlete, nor am I an exercise physiologist or medical researcher of any kind.

However, I do have a running career spanning forty-eight years and counting, and it is what I have learned during this long career that I would like to share. Over that time, I have run around 10,000 hours. As the author Malcolm Gladwell argues in his bestselling 2008 book *Outliers*, it takes 10,000 hours to become truly proficient at something or, if you like, an expert.[4] I have run 120 races of marathon distance or longer. I still run most days and have enjoyed an amazing running career on roads, in parks, and on trails. I have had no injuries that have prevented me from running, for more than a day or two, since my first year of running. I believe that, with the right approach, most people can enjoy the same experience. At the time of writing, I have run over 100,000 kilometers— around 68,000 miles—which is more than a quarter of the distance to the moon. I have felt good for all these years. It is not all down to running, I am sure, but I have not had an illness beyond minor cold and flu viruses in decades. I do not take any prescription drugs for chronic conditions. I don't run as far as I once did, and certainly not as fast, but I have as much fun as ever. You can as well.

By the way, throughout this book, I have generally referred to distances in kilometers as well as miles, as I just did in the preceding paragraph. I live in the United States, where, despite the preponderance of 5k and 10k races, distances are marked every mile, and runners talk about their pace per mile. Across the northern border in Canada or the southern border in Mexico, miles are something people only have to figure out if they visit the United States. Though some people in Britain still cling to their miles, former colonies have long joined the rest of the world in using metric distances. A book like this is not intended for readers in a particular geography, hence my decision to refer to both.

As an adult, I set out for my first run on the roads at age twenty-seven, close to ten years after my last 100-meter track race in high school. All I had done for ten years in terms of exercise was walk the course while playing mediocre golf about once a week, play some tennis (primarily doubles), hike periodically, and occasionally downhill ski. None of this is aerobic exercise that elevates the heart rate for sustained periods. Fortunately, I have never had a weight problem, thanks to my genetic makeup. All my adult life, my weight has been between 145 and 155 pounds (70kg), depending on how much running I am doing at any given time. At twenty-seven, I simply felt the urge to become fitter while I was still a relatively young adult and did not need much encouragement from my friend to join him on his daily early-morning runs. I will be quite honest: I did not expect to enjoy running on the roads, but I did hope to enjoy the benefit of improved fitness. But I quickly found I appreciated the company of fellow runners, I liked being outdoors in the early morning when it is quiet, and I enjoyed the activity as well as the fitness that came with it. I soon found I had more energy and could climb stairs without ever feeling tired, and my day-to-day living was enhanced. That was in 1974.

Back then, the worldwide running boom was not yet fully underway. I had watched the 1972 Olympic marathon in Munich on the television in my living room in the Detroit suburbs, as American Frank Shorter cruised gracefully to victory. His triumph on the last day of the Summer Olympics, when the men's marathon is traditionally held, helped lift the gloom of the tragic attack on the Israeli delegation days earlier. In 1972, as I drove around the Detroit area, I hardly ever saw someone running. I am convinced that watching Shorter winning the marathon gold in Munich played a part in my getting into running marathons a couple of years later. It was the first time I had watched a marathon.

I was disappointed when Frank failed to win at the Montreal games four years later after leading a good deal of the race, finishing second to a relatively unknown East German named Waldemar Cierpinski. It subsequently emerged that East Germany operated a state-sponsored doping program for its athletes for about twenty years from the late 1960s to the late 1980s, and some unconfirmed reports have implicated Cierpinski, a track athlete who had only started running the marathon distance in 1974.

In the second half of the 1970s, another American, Bill Rogers, was dominant on the marathon scene, winning both Boston and New York four times. He was world-class, and one wonders how he would have fared in the 1980 Summer Olympics had the United States not boycotted the Moscow games, along with sixty-five other countries, because of the Soviet Union's invasion of Afghanistan. I have no doubt that the achievements of Shorter and Rogers in the 1970s played a significant role in sparking mass participation in road running in the United States.

Where I live in Connecticut, as in other parts of the country, there is plenty of evidence that the boom in the racing scene dates to the second half of the 1970s. In the summer, I participate in a local road race series held every second week, with distances increasing from three to eleven miles, as well as in a weekly series of cross-country races. The former started in 1977 and the latter in 1979. A local winter series of races designed to prepare runners for April's Boston Marathon started in 1978. The biggest race in the area, the New Haven Road Race, started in 1977. The oldest half-marathon in the area started in 1976 as a marathon, before becoming a half-marathon a few years later as the half started to rise in popularity. My favorite 10k in the area, held every year on Mother's Day, started in 1977, and a local 50k that I have done a couple of times goes back to 1978.

Today, new races spring up every year, adding to the race calendar. On most weekends, I now have a choice of races within half an hour or so of my home, except in the dead of winter. Back in the early 1970s, however, there was not much choice at all for the few distance runners looking for a race. One wonders how they trained for a race like the Boston Marathon; I guess they grinded out the long runs on the road, mostly alone, without regular weekend races to enjoy while building their fitness. Back then, the African running revolution was not yet underway. Big city marathons with tens of thousands of runners were a thing of the future. Marathon fields were relatively small. The half-marathon, so popular today, barely existed and road races of shorter distances like the 10k were few. Runners who want to take part in road races now have so many options from which to choose. Many runners enjoy the racing scene, setting personal goals for improving their times or simply hanging out on race day with others who enjoy doing the same thing.

Rest assured, though, one does not have to participate in races at all to enjoy running. Many runners do not race; I know people who run almost every day but have no interest in races. This is perfectly fine. Running, or some other form of regular exercise, is what is important; racing is not. For me personally, participation in races has always been an integral part of my running and remains so. I enjoy the camaraderie of the race scene, the fellowship of competitors, the support of spectators at major city marathons, and, most of all, setting personal goals for an upcoming race and following a training program to raise my level of fitness to try to achieve those goals. I enjoy the motivation, not to get out and run—I would do that regardless—but to put more effort into my running to achieve a personal goal. You may not need that, which is fine.

In the next chapter, I refer to scientific studies that provide evidence that regular exercise increases one's prospects for living a healthier life, as well as living longer. Personally, I enjoy running; however, there are many people who do not like running or cannot run due to chronic injuries or other physical limitations. While this book is primarily about running as a form of exercise, cycling, swimming, rowing, many team sports, aerobics classes, and other forms of aerobic exercise can be just as beneficial in promoting cardiovascular health.

Many people think of running as an activity one does alone and that the sport is therefore not very social. While I do much of my running alone, simply for convenience, running with others can actually be a great way to socialize. If you go out for a long run with others, be it with one other person or a larger group, you will find most runners like to talk while they run. Few other sports allow concurrent social engagement as well as running does. I found that from the first day I laced up my running shoes.

So, how much time does one need to spend exercising to enjoy health benefits? The World Health Organization, or WHO (who. int), has made recommendations for levels of physical activity for various age groups from infants through to adults over the age of 65.[5] These recommendations, which WHO updated in October 2022, have been largely adopted by national health authorities in many countries, including the United Kingdom and United States. The recommendations state that adults aged 18 to 64:

- should do at least 150–300 minutes of moderate-intensity aerobic physical activity; or at least 75–150 minutes of vigorous-intensity aerobic physical activity; or an equivalent combination of moderate- and vigorous-intensity activity throughout the week
- should also do muscle-strengthening activities at moderate or greater intensity that involve all major muscle groups on two or more days a week, as these provide additional health benefits.
- may increase moderate-intensity aerobic physical activity to more than 300 minutes; or do more than 150 minutes of vigorous-intensity aerobic physical activity; or an equivalent combination of moderate- and vigorous-intensity activity throughout the week for additional health benefits.
- should limit the amount of time spent being sedentary. Replacing sedentary time with physical activity of any intensity (including light intensity) provides health benefits, and
- to help reduce the detrimental effects of high levels of sedentary behavior on health, all adults and older adults should aim to do more than the recommended levels of moderate- to vigorous-intensity physical activity

The recommendations for adults over 65 are as follows:

- Same as for adults; and
- as part of their weekly physical activity, older adults should do varied multicomponent physical activity that emphasizes functional balance and strength training at moderate or greater intensity, on three or more days a week, to enhance functional capacity and to prevent falls.

The WHO recommendations go on to note that the world's adult population is becoming less active, not more:

- More than a quarter of the world's adult population (1.4 billion adults) are insufficiently active
- Worldwide, around 1 in 3 women and 1 in 4 men do not do enough physical activity to stay healthy.
- Levels of inactivity are twice as high in high-income countries compared to low-income countries,
- There has been no improvement in global levels of physical activity since 2001
- Insufficient activity increased by 5% (from 31.6% to 36.8%) in high-income countries between 2001 and 2016.

Interestingly, a number of studies in recent years have suggested that vigorous exercise for less than seventy-five minutes per week can have some, or even similar, benefits. The common thread in many of these studies is that any amount of exercise is better than nothing. One analysis published in 2019 in the *British Journal of Sports Medicine* was titled "Is Running Associated with a Lower Risk of All-Cause, Cardiovascular and Cancer Mortality, and Is the More the Better? A Systematic Review and Meta-Analysis." This journal article got the attention of the editors of *Time* magazine, who published a summary of the findings in November 2019.[6] The study tracked more than 232,000 people from several countries over at least five years, who self-reported the amount of running they did. The mortality risk for runners, including those who ran less than seventy-five minutes per week, from any cause was 27 percent lower than for nonrunners. The mortality risk from cardiovascular disease was 30 percent lower and from cancer 23 percent lower. We will explore this subject in some depth in the next chapter.

Of course, reducing the risk of premature death is far from the only reason people choose to run regularly, myself included. Running can be a reason for heading out to the park, a trail in the woods, or the beach at sunrise; a time to be alone with nature; or an opportunity to enjoy the company of others. It can enhance one's feeling of physical and mental well-being all day long. Yes, other forms of exercise can provide comparable benefits, but running is something man has been doing since the time of primitive humans, and it has the advantage that you don't need any equipment, a partner, or a facility. All you need is running shoes and clothing suitable for the weather, and the outdoors. If you are up for it, why not run for your life?

CHAPTER 3

Running and Aging

Now that we've talked about the pleasure and some of the history of running, let's delve into the published research studies on the impact of regular exercise—mainly running—on the human body. In this chapter I'll discuss the scientific underpinnings for incorporating running or another form of exercise into your daily routine for the rest of your life.

As I previously described, I started running on a regular basis at the age of twenty-seven. My motivation was simply to raise my level of fitness, having not done regular aerobic exercise since high school. I still remembered how good I had felt when I trained for, and played, rugby in high school. Rugby is a sport where you are running most of the time.

I have met countless people through the years who started running for the same reason I did but stopped after a while because they simply did not enjoy it. Sadly, many of them did not move on and try another form of aerobic exercise instead. In my case, however, I found that I enjoyed both the activity and the company— early-morning chats with a good friend with no one around while getting the heart rate up for a sustained period. I started to enjoy the benefits as time went on: I had more energy during the day, I slept well, and I was more relaxed. These are some of the reasons I am still running on a regular basis forty-eight years later. In a way, I found it addictive.

When I was twenty-seven, I was not thinking about whether regular exercise would have a positive impact on the aging process. I did, however, start to read books and magazines on long-distance running to see what I could learn, and I encountered stories about the phenomenal achievements of some older athletes; I also read about studies of the benefits of regular exercise on the aging process. As I got older, I have taken more of an interest in this question. I have also observed how my physical condition seems to have gradually diverged from people of similar age whom I have known for a long time and who have been more sedentary over their adult lives.

None of us know what tomorrow may bring; all I know is in the forty-eight years since I started running on a regular basis, I have not had a serious illness, nothing beyond the common cold and flu viruses. I have physical examinations from time to time, including periodic stress tests on a treadmill. The only surgery I have had as an adult was to repair an old rugby-related shoulder injury not connected to running. I feel good and still enjoy running. I continue to add to my trophy cabinet well into my seventies.

When I turned seventy, I took a simple fitness test on a website: worldfitnesslevel.org. You could do the same to obtain a general idea about your current level of fitness. The results indicated I had the fitness level of the average thirty-seven-year-old, and my VO_2 max was 49 compared to an average of 36 for someone of my age. I do not have a high natural VO_2 max; however, various studies have concluded that, through regular exercise, one can improve one's VO_2 max—regardless of age.

Let's take a closer look at the benefits of regular exercise. Various studies have concluded it not only reduces the risk of cardiovascular disease; it also seems to reduce the risk of developing type 2 diabetes and some types of cancer. Studies also suggest that regular exercise is beneficial to mental health and lowering the risk of depression. I remember a middle-aged colleague years ago who arrived at work in a bad mood almost every day, never friendly. Then he took up running. Within a few months, he was transformed, arriving at work cheerful and ready for the day ahead following his morning run.

The results of numerous studies on the impact of regular exercise on aging and life expectancy confirm the benefits. In this chapter, I will highlight the results of a handful of these studies.

Starting in 1984, researchers at Stanford University in California followed 538 members of a running club and 423 healthy people who did not run for the following twenty-one years.[7] The study controlled for differences between the two groups in age, sex, smoking history, body mass index, and other factors. Over the course of the study, 5.4 percent of the runners died from heart disease or stroke and 5.6 percent from cancer. In the control group, 10.2 percent died from heart disease or stroke and 9.7 percent from cancer. The researchers predicted that the runners will live on average four years longer than the nonrunners.

In a study commissioned by the British Broadcast Corporation (BBC) and published on their website in March 2019, "Can Exercise Reverse the Aging Process,"[8] the authors, Stephen Harridge and Norman Lazarus, drew on the results of studies that "suggest regular exercise is more effective than any drug yet invented to prevent conditions facing older people, such as muscle loss. To reap the full benefits, this pattern of behavior should be laid down in a person's teens and early 20s." The key, the authors say, is exercising throughout one's adult life, into old age. As discussed further below, however, other studies suggest starting a program of regular exercise later in life can produce similar benefits. One day, we may have the full picture.

The authors note that the better health of many older people who exercise compared to those who don't, can lead one to believe that physical activity can slow down, or even reverse, the aging process. Interestingly, they argue that this is not actually the case; these older athletes are as they should be. We are wired to be physically active every day, as our hunter-gatherer ancestors were. Put another way, if, as a seventy-year-old, I had the fitness level of the average thirty-seven-year-old, it was the latter who was "old" for their age;

I was not "young" for my age. It is simply a matter that many people today are not sufficiently active.

Harridge and Lazarus go on to argue that we often confuse the effects of inactivity with the aging process and believe certain illnesses are the result of growing older when, in fact, they are not. They argue that modern sedentary lifestyles have simply speeded up the onset of cardiovascular disease (CVD), cancer, type 2 diabetes, and other illnesses. They refer to a UK National Health Service (NHS) study that revealed that 34 percent of adult men and 42 percent of adult women in England do not meet the activity guidelines of the World Health Organization (WHO) of 150 minutes of moderate-intensity aerobic physical activity or 75 minutes of vigorous-intensity aerobic physical activity per week (or some combination of the two) to which I referred in chapter 2. For older adults, the study indicated the percentage of people not meeting the activity guidelines was higher.

A study in the United States by the Centers for Disease Control and Prevention's National Center for Health Statistics (NCHS), conducted between 2010 and 2015 and published in June 2018,[9] revealed that, nationally, only 23 percent of adults aged between eighteen and sixty-four meet both the preceding exercise guidelines and a twice-a-week muscle-strengthening recommendation, though there are regional differences. Nationally, 32 percent met one but not both, and almost 45 percent did not hit either benchmark.

What if you are middle-aged or elderly and have never really exercised on a regular basis as an adult? Is it too late?

An extensive study conducted by researchers at the University of Cambridge in the United Kingdom, published in 2019, concluded that it is never too late to start exercising and to gain benefits from doing so; becoming more active in later life may lengthen one's life span "regardless of past activity levels."[10] Their study included 14,599 adults, aged forty to seventy-nine, who had enrolled in a health study on cancer and nutrition between 1993 and 1997 and whose basic health data was therefore available. The Cambridge team examined the health data at the beginning of the study and three subsequent times up to 2004 for lifestyle and other risk factors. They then followed the participants over a median period of 12.5 years from the last assessment up to 2016 in order to assess mortality. During this period, 3,148 participants died, including 950 from cardiovascular disease and 1,091 from cancer.

Where this study differed from others that have examined the impact of exercise on mortality is that it assessed levels of physical activity over an extended period and did so for a large number of participants. Many other studies included smaller numbers of participants and assessed physical activity only at a single point in time. The Cambridge researchers took into account lifestyle and risk factors, such as diet, alcohol intake, smoking status, age, height, weight, blood pressure, and medical history. They assessed physical activity levels using a validated questionnaire that covered the type of work the person did (desk job, manual work, and so on) as well as any exercise during their spare time. Information collected at periodic clinic visits supplemented the questionnaire data.

The findings demonstrated that middle-aged and older adults "stand to gain substantial longevity benefits by becoming more physically active, irrespective of past physical activity and established risk factors."[11] Even if you have never exercised, the researchers believe you stand to obtain significant benefits in terms of life expectancy from starting an exercise program. The team found this to be the case regardless of risk factors, such as overall diet quality, body mass index, blood pressure, triglycerides, and cholesterol. Interestingly, participants with preexisting cardiovascular disease and cancer stood to gain longevity benefits similar to those without these conditions. This should be a source of encouragement for people living with these conditions.

So how much exercise is required to reap these benefits? The authors answer this in terms of an increase of *1 kilojoule per kilogram per day (kJ/kg/day) per year;* a measure of energy expenditure from physical activity. To put it in perspective, an increase of this magnitude every year for five years would take an inactive person to the point of meeting the World Health Organization (WHO) minimum physical activity guidelines of 150 minutes of moderate-intensity activity per week (an average of roughly twenty minutes a day) by the fifth year. This is surely not too demanding for most of us. The authors found that gradually increasing energy expenditure to achieve the WHO minimum guidelines reduces the risk of premature mortality from any cause by 24 percent. The risk related to death from cardiovascular disease dropped by an even higher percentage. The study noted that greater longevity benefits were seen among those who increased energy expenditure beyond these minimum guidelines, as well as for those who had an exercise regimen prior to the start of the study—a reduced risk of premature mortality from any cause as high as 42 percent.

A study in the United States, published in March 2019, gives further encouragement to those who have never exercised regularly. In a paper titled "Association of Leisure-Time Physical Activity across the Adult Life Course with All-Cause and Cause-Specific Mortality,"[12] the authors, Pedro F. Maurice, Diarmuid Coughlan, and Scott P. Kelly, among others, concluded that becoming physically active sometime between forty and sixty-one years of age may provide similar benefits in terms of lower mortality risk as compared to those who have been physically active throughout adult life.

This prospective cohort study used self-reported data from a National Institutes of Health–AARP (formerly American Association of Retired Persons) Diet and Health Study in 1995 and 1996 and included 315,059 participants, 58 percent men and 42 percent women. The participants were fifty to seventy-one years of age at the time of enrollment in the study. The data analysis was conducted from March 2017 to February 2018. By then, 71,377 of the participants in the study had died, including 22,219 as a result of cardiovascular-disease-related causes (CVD) and 16,388 from cancer.

The goal of the study was to consider how patterns of regular exercise (called leisure time physical activity, or LTPA, in the study) over a wide range of ages, starting from fifteen to nineteen years and going up in bands to forty to sixty-one years, are associated with mortality from all causes, as well as from CVD and cancer. The study found that participants who had exercised regularly from their teens to their sixties had a 29 percent to 36 percent lower risk of dying from any cause over the twenty-year period covered by the study.

What surprised the researchers, however, was to find that those who only started to exercise regularly in midlife or later (forty to sixty-one years) derived broadly similar benefits in terms of lower risk of mortality from any cause to those who had continued exercising throughout adulthood. The study noted that the risk of mortality from CVD was 43 percent lower among those who started exercising regularly in this age range and was 16 percent lower with respect to cancer, compared to inactive participants.

However, the study found that most of the benefits of exercising regularly in adolescence and early adulthood in terms of risk of mortality were lost during the course of adulthood if the activity was not maintained. This is an important finding.

The authors acknowledge there are limitations to their study, including the fact that the information on the extent of participants' LTPA was obtained using historical questions and is subject to reporting errors. In addition, they acknowledge that it is uncertain whether the results can be generalized. However, the study is valuable in that it examines the impact of regular exercise on mortality from adolescence all the way up to adults in their early sixties, a much longer period than most other studies.

A key lesson from this and other studies is that it is never too late in life to start an exercise regimen and benefit from it in terms of lower risk of mortality, but once you start, you should not stop, or you will lose the benefits over time. If you are a runner, try to run for your life!

Additionally, various studies provide evidence that regular exercise can not only reduce the likelihood of the onset of certain diseases, but it can alleviate or even eliminate many chronic diseases. In a paper titled "Exercise as Medicine—Evidence for Prescribing Exercise as Therapy in 26 Different Chronic Diseases,"[13] the authors, B. K. Pedersen and B. Saltin, discuss the beneficial impact of exercise on various chronic conditions, including some psychological and neurological conditions, based on an extensive study of medical literature. They note modest evidence of the benefits of exercise for people suffering from depression, anxiety, and stress. They go on to note strong evidence of the benefits of exercise in lowering the risk of developing dementia, though there are few studies that analyze the effects of exercise on people who already have a diagnosis of dementia. There is, however, good evidence of the benefits of exercise for those living with Parkinson's disease.

Metabolic syndrome is known to be a precursor of type 2 diabetes; several large-scale studies show that physical activity can prevent the onset of metabolic syndrome and therefore greatly reduce the risk of developing type 2 diabetes. For many people living with type 2 diabetes, the studies add, exercise can be an important component of their treatment regimen.

In the area of metabolic diseases, Pedersen and Saltin note that regular exercise has been shown to have a beneficial effect on the lipid profile of the blood (including cholesterol levels). This could contribute to the reduction in the risk of cardiovascular disease mentioned in the next paragraph. Studies indicate that the greater the intensity of exercise or time spent exercising, the greater the benefit on the lipid profile.

The authors go on to note benefits from regular exercise in the area of cardiovascular diseases. Studies have noted the benefits of exercise in lowering blood pressure, reducing the incidence of hypertension. Hypertension is a risk factor for stroke and heart failure. The benefits of exercise for people with coronary heart disease, and even heart failure, are well documented; the authors refer to extensive studies on patients with these conditions. They go on to discuss the benefits of exercise for patients with various types of pulmonary disease, as well as certain forms of musculoskeletal disorders, such as osteoporosis, which I touch on further below.

Pedersen and Saltin's paper refers to growing evidence that regular physical activity reduces the risk of developing a number of common types of cancer, as well as improving the survival prospects for people with breast cancer and colon cancer. They refer to several studies that confirm the benefits of being physically active for many cancer patients in terms of reduced fatigue and improved emotional well-being and quality of life in general.

These are some of the diseases that Pedersen and Saltin review in their paper. A key takeaway from their analysis is that regular exercise not only reduces one's risk of premature death, but it can lead to a longer health span as well—being able to enjoy life without the burden of chronic disease. Needless to say, anyone who is suffering from any of the conditions they discuss in the paper should only start an exercise program under the guidance of a physician working in the particular field.

An article published in the UK in January 2020 on the BBC website refers to the results of tests carried out by researchers from Barts and University College London on 138 novice entrants in the London Marathon.[14] The findings indicated "over six months of training, their arteries regained some youthful elasticity, which should reduce the risk of heart attacks and strokes. And their blood pressure fell as much as if they had been prescribed pills." These were not elite runners: the subjects completed the marathon in four and a half to five and a half hours. The researchers suggest that training for and running the marathon took about four years off their "vascular age."

What about running as a way of mitigating the onset of osteoporosis? It is well known that weight-bearing and resistance exercises (like lifting weights and rowing) are good for bone health and countering bone loss. Running is a weight-bearing form of exercise, as you are on your feet, and this should promote healthy bones. There is some debate as to whether a brisk walk is better than running for bone health or whether short, fast runs are better than long-distance running. Swimming and cycling, while beneficial for cardiovascular fitness and building certain muscle groups, are not weight-bearing forms of exercise.

I would, however, caution anyone who has been diagnosed with osteoporosis not to engage in a high-impact form of exercise like running without obtaining medical advice first. While Pedersen and Saltin refer to research that discusses the potential benefits, the risks of stress fractures are higher for people with bone loss. I have fallen several times while running—on the roads when I accidentally planted a foot in a pothole or slipped on mud or ice I had not seen, as well as on trails when my foot caught a root or small rock. The risks of breaking bones in a fall need to be weighed against the benefits of promoting bone health from running. Walking could be a better alternative for those with osteoporosis.

Finally, let us delve a little further into the impact of regular exercise on cognitive functioning, as several studies have shown it to be quite significant, especially for older adults. In a paper titled "The Positive Impact of Physical Activity on Cognition during Adulthood: A Review of Underlying Mechanisms, Evidence, and Recommendations,"[15] the authors, John J. Ratley and James E. Loehor, reported findings from their review of numerous studies of the influence of physical activity on brain function among adults. Their review notes that exercise benefits brain function in adults, particularly frontal-lobe-mediated processes. Among the more important conclusions they document are the following:

Exercise is associated with improvements in brain function and cognition throughout life.

Even a single bout of exercise can improve reaction times and speed of information processing, among other cognitive functions.

- A short-term exercise program, measured in weeks, can improve information processing and decision-making abilities.
- Regular physical activity is associated with better cognition, and this is preserved into later life if one exercised in early and middle adulthood.
- Older adults who exercise perform better on tasks involving planning, scheduling, and working memory.
- Regular physical activity affects emotional satisfaction and quality of life.

Though certainly not a condition that occurs only in older adults, it is worth noting that regular exercise can also help one deal with clinical depression. In 2000, M. Babyak and colleagues conducted a ten-month study on 156 adult volunteers with major depressive disorder (MDD).[16] The volunteers were randomly assigned to one of three groups: the first group were given a four-month program of regular aerobic exercise, the second group were given a four-month course of a common antidepressant prescription medication, and the third group were given the exercise program and the medication. After four months, all three groups showed significant improvement, which was comparable across the three groups.

A further assessment was performed six months later. Volunteers in the exercise-only group had significantly lower relapse rates than volunteers who received the medication. The authors concluded that exercising is highly therapeutic, especially if the exercise regimen is continued.

This study followed patients already diagnosed with MDD. It stands to reason, however, that those of us who exercise regularly are less likely to become clinically depressed. A number of other studies have found this to be the case.

To conclude, the consequences of sedentary lifestyles on how we age are becoming more apparent as life expectancy increases with the benefit of modern medicine to manage CVD, cancer, type 2 diabetes, and other conditions common in the elderly. Unfortunately, many people are living their later years with one or more chronic conditions; while their life span has increased compared to earlier times, their health span, and ability to enjoy life to the full, has not. Regular exercise is a cornerstone for living a longer and healthier life, whether it is running or some other activity.

I recall hearing about the passing, at the end of 2021, of a long-standing member of the running club to which I once belonged in South Africa. His name was Budge Rens, and he was ninety-four when he died. Budge was primarily a cross-country runner, a very good one, and competed for seventy years, from the age of nineteen until the age of eighty-nine. He even took part in the national cross-country championship at the age of eighty-nine in the eighty-five to eighty-nine category. He told club mates the following year that "the wheels fell off," and he was forced to go out walking for exercise rather than running, but he did this regularly until not long before his death. Budge is a fine example of someone living a long life, including a long health span.

One does not, however, need to set out to be the local age-group champion—unless one wants to be—all one needs is regular exercise in small bouts several times a week. According to the WHO guidelines discussed earlier in this chapter, twenty minutes a day of brisk walking or gently riding a stationary bicycle in the gym will do fine. If you are up for running twenty minutes a day instead, four days a week will meet the guideline, as will some other form of exercise that raises the heart rate. I have long held the view that if I only have time to run for ten minutes on a particular day before taking a shower and getting dressed to head out, I will do it, as even ten minutes is better than nothing.

Most importantly, while some studies suggest that the earlier in adult life one embarks on a lifelong exercise program the better, other studies provide strong evidence that it is never, ever too late to start. That is good news.

CHAPTER 4

Running and Psychology

For my entire career I have worked in an office sitting at a desk, just as millions of people do every day, though at various times I have worked in locations where there was an opportunity to run during my lunch break. Either I was a short drive from a sports facility where I would go to run a few times a week, or I had access to changing and shower facilities in the office complex. Most of these lunchtime runs were with a small group of work colleagues and were usually around twenty to thirty minutes in duration. We often ran pretty hard.

I loved these runs, in part because it was a social activity away from the office in the middle of the day, but mostly because when I returned to my desk an hour later, I felt like I was starting a new day. I felt invigorated, as fresh as I had at the start of the work day. No doubt part of this is physical, however, part is psychological, of that I am convinced. In this chapter we will delve into some of the psychological benefits of running.

Running and other forms of exercise increase blood flow to all parts of the body, including the brain, and cause the body to produce the hormones serotonin and dopamine. Studies indicate that serotonin is associated with mood stability and a feeling of contentment, while dopamine has a positive effect on our levels of motivation. Is this why, after my lunchtime runs, I felt a "runner's high" rather than the sluggish feeling one sometimes has after sitting down for a midday meal?

Another factor, if you are outside running in a city park or even a tree-lined suburban street, as I was with most of these midday runs, is the beneficial effect of what the Japanese call *shinrin-yoku*, literally translated as forest bathing, a natural therapy from simply connecting with nature. Rest assured that you do not have to run in the middle of the day for feelings of *shinrin-yoku*; any time of the day when you are running in a park or on a trail you will enjoy these benefits. I just found the midday impact more profound after spending a whole morning indoors in an office setting. A recent article in National Wildlife magazine[17] discussed research into how hearing birdsong while on a trail raises people's spirits, and the greater the number of bird species that are singing, the more content people are.

In chapter 3, I referred to studies about how physical activity benefits brain functioning, including information processing, reaction times, and decision making, and how cognitive improvements are preserved as one ages. Another study I mentioned demonstrated how powerful regular exercise can be in dealing with depression. Many studies have concluded that running and other forms of aerobic exercise have a positive effect on our emotions and sense of well-being. How often do you see someone finishing a run looking angry?

A review of 116 studies on the relationship between running and mental health, published in 2020,[18] refers to some studies that found a "positive association with higher self-identity and low levels of depression" while others found that marathon training had a positive impact on "self-esteem and psychological coping." Further studies the authors reviewed found that subjects who had taken up running reported "better emotional well-being, relief of tension, self-image and self-confidence," among other psychological benefits.

I have long found running to be a great way to manage stress and develop resilience, leaving me better equipped to deal with difficult situations. When one is faced with a problem at work or a crisis at home, it is not always possible to just drop everything and go out for a run, but I always look for the first opportunity to do so. Returning from a run, even a short one, I have a clearer head and refreshed perspective on the situation; I am thus more relaxed and better able to cope.

In later chapters I talk about my interest in running ultramarathons earlier in my career. I am not talking about 100 milers, rather races longer than the standard marathon but no more than double that distance. While I am not for minute suggesting everyone needs to run ultramarathons, I do believe doing so has helped me strengthen my will to succeed in daily life. Anyone who enters a 5k race, or even a 10k, expects to finish, and the majority of us expect to do so without having to walk. Yes, we may stop to take a drink at a refreshment station and walk a few paces before getting back into our stride but, barring an injury, will not think of quitting.

This changes as one moves up to running longer distances like the marathon or beyond. If you look at the results of a marathon you will usually note a number of names with DNF (did not finish) at the end of the list of finishers. With large scale events like big city marathons, there are sometimes pages of DNFs. Why is this? Some will have picked up, or aggravated, an injury during the race (as happened to me once in a marathon early in my career). Others will have not put in the necessary preparation to run the distance and will drop out due to extreme fatigue. But some could have finished but lacked the willpower to press on when the going got tough, the legs became tired, and the mind started to question the sense of doing this.

Some of us are wired with a greater level of determination than others. I have never seriously considered quitting during a race other than the one occasion when I had no choice. On the other hand, I concede I have never attempted any form of extreme sports, including running very long distances, where my willpower might be severely tested. I admire those who climb the highest mountains, swim vast distances in open water, or run all day and all night to reach a finish line, but this is not for me. I am sure, however, that distance running has strengthened my determination to succeed—to never give up—and that transfers to other aspects of life.

As I say, I have run 120 races of marathon distance or longer. In chapter 10 I explain how, in a marathon, you will inevitably "run out of gas" and have to fight through fatigue. My first marathon, which I described in chapter 1, was a grueling experience, but I had a friend encouraging me to keep going as fatigue set in. If he had not been there to spur me on, I have little doubt I would have started walking on the hills in the second half and not made the four-hour cutoff to earn a medal. Today, that sort of encouragement from a support crew is rarely possible, yet I learned from my early experience that I could push through the fatigue and keep running. I learned that if I was forced to walk in a marathon on a steep hill, I should pick a landmark ahead of me, perhaps a tree or a lamppost or a mailbox, and allow myself to walk for a minute at most to the landmark and then will myself to start running again as soon as I reached that point. This takes discipline, but it did wonders for improving my level of determination. When I am faced with an unpleasant task, one that I would prefer to delay or avoid altogether, I try to think of that last hour of a marathon, or an ultramarathon, when it takes all my willpower to stay committed to getting to the finish line to set a personal best time, beat a rival, or win an award.

I have never lacked the motivation to lace up my shoes and head out for a run; the fact is I look forward to it. However, some casual runners who take up running for the health benefits we talked about in the last chapter but who have no interest in racing, let alone running marathons, have told me that making themselves get out of bed, or off the couch, to head out for a run has raised their level of determination in other aspects of daily life. I am not surprised.

What about the time we actually spend running, once we are out the door? I remember being asked once by a top amateur tennis player what one "does with the mind" when running. Isn't running boring? When playing tennis, one is thinking about shot selection and execution, or anticipating the shot the opponent is going to play next; the mind is constantly active. So let us take a look at what the mind does, or can do, while we are out there running. In this regard running with companions and running alone are quite different.

I have always found runners like to talk while they run—at least most do. Of course, the nature of the conversation will be different if you are running with a friend whom you meet for a run a few times a week, as in my case when I first started running regularly, as opposed to running with someone with whom you do not normally run. In the latter case, I find the early conversation almost always revolves around our respective running experiences. The conversation will be different again if you run with a group, something I enjoy very much. The key thing is running can be a sociable sport, except, of course, if one is running hard, close to one's limit, in a race.

Running alone, especially if one is not listening to music, affords all kinds of possibilities. I have met runners who use the time to meditate. Though I think of meditation as requiring sitting with legs crossed in a quiet place and breathing deeply, there are in fact many forms of meditation. What one can do on a run is expunge all thoughts and let the mind "free-wheel." Some say this is a form of meditation; to me it simply gives my mind a rest and allows the body to do the work. When a thought enters the mind, I try to let it go.

On the other hand, we can use the time spent running alone to think, to concentrate, be that to plan the day ahead, consider the options for dealing with a problem, or simply reflect. When I was involved in administering professional examinations, I remember using a quiet early morning run to think through the mechanics of a question I was going to put to the students.

However, I would be remiss not to offer a word of caution. You should always be aware of your surroundings to protect your safety, wherever you run. Running and talking to someone alongside you is a distraction. Running and thinking about a question for a written test is a distraction. So, in a way, is losing your thoughts. I know this might seem contradictory, but one needs to find the right balance between being alert to possible safety risks and enjoying the mental aspects of being out for a run. The whole of chapter 6 is further devoted to running safety.

Let's now look at the connection between running and a good night's sleep. It is well established that getting sufficient sleep on a regular basis is essential for our physical and mental well-being. Most of us have a bad night from time to time, but millions of people suffer from insomnia; in many cases the cause is unclear. What we do know, however, is that regular exercise enhances the quality of our sleep, including the REM sleep thought to be critical for memory.

I have never had much trouble sleeping (other than when changing time zones, and I find exercise helps with that too.) From talking to runners over many years, most of whom say they sleep well, I am convinced that my running routine is a factor. If I run, even though I usually run in the morning, I am tired by the time I go to bed. Running makes it easier to fall asleep and helps me stay asleep.

I have also found I need more sleep when I step up the amount of running I do when training for a marathon, up to an additional hour if I am doing long runs regularly. This is typical with long distance runners. In addition, many people taking up regular exercise for the first time and who are still adapting to their new routine find they need extra sleep. The important point for all of us is not to deprive our bodies and our minds of the sleep needed. Sleep deprivation affects our ability to concentrate, our mood, our energy level, and affects our reaction times and leaves us more accident prone. Regular exercise is a great tonic to produce a good night's sleep.

By the way, in recent years I have learned how bad it is for us to sit at a desk all day long, like I did most days for decades, even though sometimes I might walk across town to attend a meeting or go to the airport to fly to another city to visit a client, and therefore moved around to some extent. The COVID-19 pandemic ended that sort of routine in 2020 as virtually all meetings moved online. This meant I was at a desk looking at my computer screen even when attending meetings. This compelled me to finally invest in a standing desk, which I love. I spend more time standing and less time sitting. A good deal of this book was written standing up. I heartily recommend standing desks, of which there are many varieties at different price points.

So, to conclude, numerous studies have confirmed regular exercise has psychological as well as physiological benefits; these include helping us deal with stress and sleep better, strengthening our self-discipline and willpower, and building our self-confidence. Isn't that worth it?

CHAPTER 5

Running and Cardiovascular Health

H aving taken a look into a number of scientific studies exploring the many health benefits of including a form of aerobic exercise as part of your daily routine, I am now going to offer some cautionary advice, because exercise is not without risk, especially when unsupervised. More than anything, one needs a healthy heart to run.

A few years ago, during my annual physical examination, I mentioned to the physician I thought I should visit my cardiologist for a stress test, having not had one for a few years. A stress test involves walking and/or running on a treadmill at a gradually increasing pace while one's heart rhythm and blood pressure are monitored. The objective is to monitor how well the heart functions when exercising. I have, as a matter of choice, periodically undergone stress tests since around the age of forty.

He replied, "Why bother? You have a stress test every day when you run."

While I can see his point, my daily runs are unsupervised and I plan to continue periodically having monitored stress tests out of an abundance of caution. If you exercise regularly, and that is what I am recommending, I believe it is in your best interest to periodically have a comprehensive checkup to monitor that all is well with the body and especially the cardiovascular system. Whether this includes a resting electrocardiogram (EKG), a stress test, echocardiogram, or other tests is up to you and your doctors.

In 1977, the decade of the running boom, an American named Jim Fixx published a book called *The Complete Book of Running*, which sold over a million copies.[19] Everyone who ran at the time, myself included, knew about the book, and many of us read it. He published a second book on running in 1980 and an autobiographical book in 1982. Jim had started running in 1967 at the age of thirty-five when he weighed over two hundred pounds or roughly ninety kilograms and smoked two packs of cigarettes a day. Over time, as a regular runner and marathoner, he lost around a third of that weight and stopped smoking. The inside cover of his first book states that he ran ten miles (sixteen kilometers) a day. Then in July 1984, he collapsed and died of a heart attack during his daily run, at the age of fifty-two.

An autopsy revealed that three of Fixx's coronary arteries were substantially blocked; one of the three was 95 percent blocked. He had a number of risk factors for coronary artery disease: firstly, a genetic predisposition, as his father had died of a heart attack at age forty-three, having survived an earlier attack, and secondly, lifestyle factors—at least up to the time he started running, he was overweight and a heavy smoker. Whether Fixx underwent a medical examination before taking up running or had regular examinations during the seventeen years that he ran regularly, I do not know. I have to believe, however, that with his coronary arteries as blocked as they were, he would have had some warning signs while running that all was not well in the last year or two before he died. His impaired cardiovascular capacity would surely have affected his running performance compared to earlier years. Back in 1984, bypass surgery to replace blocked arteries was being performed regularly with much success, but it seems he never had this procedure.

Jim Fixx became a decent runner, qualifying for and finishing the Boston Marathon, but he was not a star. Ryan Shay, who collapsed and died at age twenty-eight during the US Olympic Trials Marathon in Central Park, New York, in November 2007, was. His death shocked the running community in the United States. Following a successful athletic career at the University of Notre Dame, he ran professionally and was the USA Track and Field (USATF) champion at the 15k, 20k, half-marathon (twice), and marathon between 2003 and 2005. He was an accomplished middle- and long-distance runner. Autopsy results indicated he died of cardiac arrhythmia due to a preexisting enlarged heart. (Jim Fixx also had a congenitally enlarged heart.)

Would an examination by a cardiologist have revealed warning signs for Shay, a superbly fit athlete? I am not sure. For an elite runner to collapse and die during a race is very rare, but this incident does bring home the importance of cardiovascular health and the role of regular physical examinations.

A couple of summers ago, I arrived for one of the local weekly cross-country races I do frequently to see a male runner had collapsed near where one signs up and pays the small fee, apparently upon completing his warm-up run and presumably as a result of cardiac arrest. He seemed unresponsive but was receiving treatment from volunteers, including an emergency room doctor who just happened to be on the scene to run the race. From a distance, it looked like they were applying cardiopulmonary resuscitation (CPR), and I heard they were going to use an automated external defibrillator (AED) device that the race director carried in his vehicle. An ambulance soon arrived, and the paramedics appeared to restore a heartbeat, as his color improved. They stabilized the patient and transported him to the local hospital. Two weeks later, he was back, looking well, not to run but just to thank those who had helped him.

I do not know him, exactly what happened, or anything about his medical history, but he is a regular at local races and is not overweight in the slightest. He would be in his fifties. Yet he collapsed at the end of a warm-up run, not even a race, fortunately where people were gathered and not somewhere deep in the surrounding woods running alone. Most of us who race regularly have heard the wail of ambulance sirens or have seen a runner collapsed on the side of the road or trail receiving attention, as I did at a recent trail race. The theme of this book is my belief that there are immeasurable benefits to running on a regular basis; however, there are health risks with exercise, and we need to be aware of them and manage them sensibly.

Before starting a program of regular exercise, I urge you to undergo a complete physical examination to make sure it is safe for you to elevate your heart rate for a sustained period. Again, it is not for me to say what this examination should include; consult with your personal physician or a specialized exercise physiologist. Needless to say, the older you are when starting an exercise regimen, the more critical this is. And once you start an exercise program, I encourage you to undergo physical examinations at regular intervals.

To emphasize my point, let me tell you about a personal experience concerning my cardiac rhythm. In late 2018, a life insurance policy I'd had for a number of years was about to mature, and I looked to extend or replace it. This required a basic physical examination conducted by an examiner sent to my home by the insurance company. This included various blood tests. One of the tests was something for which I had never been tested before, called NT-proBNP. It is a peptide (small protein) continually produced in small quantities in the heart and in larger quantities when the heart is having to work harder. It is commonly used to detect and monitor the severity of heart failure. My reading came in at around 1,000 pg/ml, which is several times higher than normal ranges. I did not for a minute think I was suffering heart failure, as I was running as regularly as ever without difficulty, nor did I show any other signs of heart failure. Nevertheless, I was concerned about it and spoke to my doctor, who said he would never use this particular test on healthy individuals, as there is no reason to do so, and in view of my exercise regimen, I should not be concerned about the result. I also contacted a leading cardiologist, who expressed the same opinion and said my results were not that high, even if outside a normal range. Accordingly, I kept up my running and moved on.

In the months that followed, especially during the warmer months when I was taking part in local races of up to 10 miles (16 kilometers) regularly and winning my division, I noticed, at times, my legs wanted to go faster than my breathing could accommodate, a strange feeling of limitation for me. Through that summer I was, in theory, becoming fitter by running regularly and racing frequently, but my times were not improving. I also seemed to labor on hills in a way I was not used to; I have long found hills to be a strength of my running. I put it down to the effects of aging. Though I was still competitive on the local running scene in the seventy age-group, I was simply unable to run faster than around nine minutes a mile, equivalent to around five minutes forty seconds per kilometer.

At my next annual physical examination during the winter that followed, an EKG showed my resting pulse to be around fifty beats per minute, as it has been for years, but detected atrial fibrillation (A-fib). This is an abnormal heart rhythm with rapid and irregular beats of the atria (the two upper chambers) of the heart. With a normal heartbeat the atria and ventricles (the two lower chambers) work in sync; with A-fib they do not. According to published studies, it affects 2 to 3 percent of the population of Europe and North America, with higher percentages in people over sixty and up to 14 percent in people over eighty. It is not uncommon for there to be no symptoms and for it to be detected by a routine EKG, as in my case. The doctor referred me to a cardiologist, whom I visited a week later. A second EKG confirmed my heart was still in A-fib.

This condition can increase the risk of stroke but, after inquiring into my general health, lifestyle, and family background, the cardiologist concluded my risk was relatively low compared to many cases. However, he recommended I undergo an echocardiogram as a precaution. We also discussed the fact that my running speed had dropped significantly in recent years, something I had attributed to aging, as is borne out in studies of the impact of aging on athletic performance discussed in chapter 13. The cardiologist said aging would be a factor in the decline, but the fact that my heart was in A-fib would also undoubtedly be a factor. How long this had been the case we do not know, but I suspect it could have been a year or perhaps longer.

An echocardiogram, which I underwent the following week, is an ultrasound examination of the heart. It gives the cardiologist a wealth of information about the structure and functioning of the heart. This scan detected minor mitral regurgitation (a slightly leaking valve), probably the result of aging, nothing else. The cardiologist told me correction of this is a routine procedure, but my case was "a mile away" from requiring intervention.

He said I basically had two choices regarding the A-fib: simply monitor the condition or undergo a cardioversion procedure. Cardioversion is the application of a direct current electrical shock to the heart, performed while the patient is sedated, to restore a normal heart rhythm. I was told the procedure rarely fails, the unknown is whether the heart rhythm will remain normal with the passage of time; sometimes it does, sometimes not. I elected to undergo the procedure.

Prior to the procedure, I was prescribed anticoagulants (blood-thinning medication) for four weeks. The procedure was performed in early March 2020, shortly before hospitals in my area stopped performing elective procedures because of the COVID-19 crisis. The first shock was successful. (If it is not, a second, stronger shock will generally be applied.) I did not feel any different immediately afterward or indeed in the days and weeks that followed. I took a five-day break from running and then started again cautiously.

Initially, I did not feel stronger, still finding the hills hard work, but as the weeks went by, I noticed an improvement in my times and the way I felt running hills. I had a follow-up consultation two weeks later, which confirmed my heart was still in a normal rhythm, but I already knew that, as I had in the meantime purchased a simple, battery-operated home EKG device that works with an app on a smartphone, so I could monitor my heart rate regularly.

From what I have read, there are a number of possible causes of A-fib, including genetics, hypertension, tobacco and alcohol use, and a sedentary lifestyle, none of which seemed to apply to me.

I wondered if years and years of running and racing might be a cause and found a meta-analysis that looked into a possible connection between exercise and A-fib.[20] The analysis examined twenty-two studies involving over 650,000 subjects. The authors concluded that moderate exercise reduces the risk of A-fib in both men and women. Interestingly, however, they found that more intense exercise significantly reduces the risk in women but *significantly increases* the risk of A-fib in men. I have not been able to find any literature that explains why there is a gender difference.

I therefore believe my A-fib is probably a result of all my running, probably the intense effort I put into speed workouts and racing. At visits to cardiologists over the years, I have been told I have a "runner's heart," which includes mild enlargement of the left atrium as well as a slower-than-average heart rate, a physiological adaptation to years of regular exercise. I have also been told by other long-distance runners that they have experienced episodes of the heart beating irregularly from time to time. I have myself experienced this, but rarely. This has happened to me most commonly during, or in the days following, a hard race, usually a shorter distance like 5k or 10k rather than a marathon. During these episodes, I struggle to maintain my pace on hills, but I never became concerned about the condition as it has always disappeared in a day or two. The last time I recall this happening was around the time of the elevated NT-proBNP test. Was this a precursor to A-fib? I simply do not know.

Having been diagnosed with A-fib, I wondered if there might be a relationship between elevated levels of NT-proBNP and this condition. A relatively small study of outpatients with A-fib at one university hospital in 2006 concluded that A-fib was associated with increased levels of NT-proBNP in both patients with underlying structural cardiac disease *and those without underlying disease*.[21] Interestingly, the median level of NT-proBNP in the latter group, without symptoms of heart failure, was similar to my level in 2018. There is therefore some evidence that A-fib can be an independent determinant of elevated levels of NT-proBNP, and this might explain my out-of-range result.

I was also interested whether endurance exercise, in the absence of A-fib, can cause higher levels of NT-proBNP, perhaps as a result of stress on the heart. There are a number of studies on athletes, ranging from finishers in a half-marathon to competitors in the three-week Giro d'Italia cycle race, that confirm endurance exercise does lead to higher-than-normal NT-proBNP, at least in the short term. Follow-up testing in some studies suggests this is temporary and that levels return to normal with rest.

Whether the adaptation of the heart to a lifetime of long-distance running can result in long-term elevated levels of NT-proBNP is not known as far as I can tell. Perhaps not, as a follow-up NT-proBNP test—some five months after the cardioversion procedure restored the normal heart rhythm—came in at 230 pg/ml, well within the normal range. A month later, I visited my cardiologist for a periodic stress EKG test, which was also completely normal.

By the way, the life insurance company declined my application purely on the grounds of the out-of-range NT-proBNP test. The fact that I run most days, eat a relatively healthy diet, have never smoked, have a low body mass index, and was not taking any medication to manage chronic conditions was apparently not relevant to their decision-making. The agent told me insurance companies routinely reject people with high NT-proBNP as there is a presumption that they have symptoms of heart failure. The echocardiogram and recent stress EKG test confirmed what I my instincts told me from the enjoyment I get from my running—I do not have structural cardiac issues or indications of heart failure.

Why am I telling you all this? Firstly, I strongly advocate having a periodic physical examination. Schedule one, I repeat, before starting a running program, but continue to do so even if you have been running for years and feel perfectly healthy. You never know what you may learn, and if any medical issues are brought to light, you can address them. Secondly, I wanted to get some information out about the NT-proBNP test, as most runners, in fact, most people will not have heard about this test or its purpose. It is not generally used as part of routine physical examinations of healthy individuals, at least in the United States as best I can tell except, it seems, when applying for life insurance.

As the cardiologist had suggested would happen, as the weeks went by after the cardioversion procedure, my running got stronger, especially on hills. It is hard to compare times, as there were no races in the months following the procedure because of the pandemic, so I could not go out and run a race that I did the previous year and compare the time. My belief, however, is that the improvement was at least thirty seconds a mile, around twenty seconds per kilometer. Through the summer of 2020, running in virtual races of similar distances to those I ran in 2019, but on my own without fellow competitors around me, I was consistently faster.

I felt much better on hills than I had for a couple of years. I have a circular course near my home which I run two or three times a month. The course is around 8 miles or 12 kilometers and includes a long hill, quite steep in parts. I always run this hill hard. In late 2016, as I picked up my training in advance of my seventieth birthday, I was running this hill in 4 minutes and 20 to 30 seconds, with a best of 4:19. My times were similar in 2017, but by 2019 they had slipped to around the 5-minute mark, as they were in 2020 up to the time of the cardioversion procedure. In the months following, I got the times on this hill back down to where they were in late 2016, even though I was nearly four years older.

I suspect my heartbeat was irregular for much of 2019, and this affected my times. Even though I was winning division prizes regularly at local races, I was not at my best, and, looking back now, I know it. Consider monitoring your heart rate regularly at home using a smart watch or a mobile EKG device linked to a smartphone app. If I had done this, I would have known about my A-fib earlier.

Let me tell you about another senior male runner with A-fib. He is a couple of years younger than I am, and we see one another at many of the local races I enter. We have long been about the same speed and have competed for several years. As we emerged from the worst of the pandemic and races started up again, I noticed he was unable to keep pace with me even though he puts in more training than I do. Then he told me one day his heart is in A-fib, and I knew why. While taking blood thinners to reduce stroke risk, he had not elected to try a cardioversion procedure.

Next, I would like to say a little about colds and influenza (flu). While exercise does strengthen the immune system and one's ability to fight viruses, we all succumb to winter viruses from time to time. A long time ago, I remember being told about the "neck down rule" to determine whether it is safe to run while fighting a winter virus. If you look at popular websites on health like webmd.com or livestrong.com, you will find articles containing similar advice. Quite simply, if you have a head cold, with symptoms like nasal congestion and sneezing—symptoms that do not affect the body from the neck down—some consider it safe to run. Of course, you may not feel like running with a heavy cold, and I would urge you to not do so if the only reason is, say, to continue a streak of days of not missing a run. If you don't feel like running, you probably should not.

In contrast, if you have the flu, which is often accompanied by a mild to moderate fever—symptoms from the neck down—you should definitely not run, as it can be dangerous. The reason I am including this discussion in a chapter on cardiovascular health is because doing so can strain the heart and be fatal in extreme cases. Flu is a respiratory illness caused by a virus, and the fever is part of the body's mechanism to fight the virus. The best thing to do, in my opinion, is rest and allow the body to recover. With a fever, even a mild one, the heart rate increases; exercising and making the heart work harder will put added strain on the heart and can result in heart failure in extreme cases.

Early in my running career, a leading runner over the shorter distances on the road, whom I knew vaguely, collapsed and died following a race. His brother said he had recently "recovered" from a bout of flu. This left an impression on me. If I have any flu-like symptoms, I stop all forms of exercise. When I feel I have recovered, I start again by running slowly, so slowly that I look like an absolute beginner. I work up from there over several days—better safe than sorry.

Twice I have entered a race but not taken part because symptoms of a virus appeared the night before. A few years ago, I was visiting Johannesburg and was in town over a weekend when a popular 10k takes place, so I entered it. I woke up in the middle of the night before the event with a slight fever, nothing serious, which was still with me the morning of the race. I dismissed any thoughts of running a 10k, got dressed, and went out for a walk instead. This was not a big deal, but a similar experience in 1994 was.

I had trained to run the London Marathon for the first time and flew to London for a couple of days just to run the race. On the Saturday afternoon prior to race day, I went to the marathon expo, checked in, and collected my race number. I felt fine and ready for the experience of running one of the world's great city marathons; I slept well and woke up early to go to the station to take a train to the start in Greenwich but soon realized I was feeling slightly off: no apparent fever but aching muscles. You want aching muscles at the end of a marathon not before you start, so I made the agonizing decision not to run the marathon. I went back to bed in my hotel room for a while, got dressed in street clothes, had breakfast downstairs, and then walked fifteen minutes or so to a point near the finish in front of Buckingham Palace to watch the race. It was a cold, windy day. I was very disappointed after months of training, but you cannot put a price on your health. As it turned out, it took me about a week to throw off the virus before I could run again, even though the symptoms were mild. I had been on a number of flights in the two weeks prior, so I probably picked up a virus in my travels. I returned to London the following year, had a good race, and completed the marathon in 3 hours, 6 minutes, a time I have not beaten since.

What about COVID-19 and its various mutations, which can affect the lungs, as well as the heart in some cases? In the years to come, research on the impact of COVID-19 on exercise will no doubt be carried out and published. All I can say at this time, if you have contracted COVID-19 and recovered, is to consult with your medical team before starting or resuming an exercise program and follow their advice.

Finally, I would like to briefly mention the connection between weight and cardiovascular disease and offer some thoughts on running or another form of aerobic exercise, as an element of a program to control weight and improve one's overall health. It is well established that above-normal body weight, and especially obesity (body mass index or "BMI" above 30), is a risk factor for heart disease. More blood vessels are needed to supply blood in larger quantities than a slim person would require in order to feed the additional fat cells. This leads to added strain on the heart. Overweight people also tend to have high blood lipids, especially triglycerides; this is believed to increase the risk of heart disease. Obesity can cause inflammation, which can lead to atherosclerosis, the buildup of plaque on the walls of the arteries, thereby reducing blood flow, and can lead to a heart attack.

Obesity is also a risk factor for diseases that are themselves the source of risk factors for heart disease. The primary ones are hypertension and type-2 diabetes. Both conditions are fortunately treatable with lifestyle changes, medications, or a combination.

Let me stress that I do not have any expertise in this area and no personal experience. Genetically, I am not predisposed to gaining weight. It is well established that genetics is a major factor in determining who is susceptible to obesity and who is not. I truly admire anyone who wants to incorporate regular exercise into a program to try to shed weight. All I would say is be extremely careful before starting. Have a physical examination and obtain professional advice about starting a regimen, whether daily walking, running, or something else.

I watch what I eat but not with a view to lose weight. I do know, however, from many years of running that my weight drops, despite increasing my calorie intake, as I step up the training to prepare for a marathon or ultramarathon. Many fellow runners have told me they experience the same thing. Over the months of preparing for an ultramarathon, I have lost close to 5 percent of my body weight, and my BMI of around 20 is at the lower end of "normal" to begin with. In my case, without a doubt, the more I exercise, the more weight I lose.

Some studies indicate regular exercise can contribute to weight loss as well as a reduction in risk factors for cardiovascular disease; others are inconclusive. I suspect this all comes down to genetics. People have told me they tried running to lose weight but did not do so; it seems some of us will simply not shed weight from exercise alone. There is, however, stronger evidence that physical activity plays a key role in *preventing* weight gain, including in individuals who have lost weight through dieting.

My advice to anyone who wants to include exercise as a component of a weight-loss program is to not be deterred if medical advice confirms it is safe for you to do so. You will surely gain the other benefits that running can bring you—more energy, a sense of mental well-being, better sleep and the prospect of improved overall health. And if you are able to lose weight by changing your diet and reducing your calorie intake, numerous studies show that regular exercise, especially running, will help enormously in not putting that weight back on again.

Having discussed safety from a health standpoint, let us now turn to the question of staying safe when we venture out on to the roads or the trails or a park, and managing the risks that come with that.

CHAPTER 6

Running Safety

S afety is paramount; if you want to run for your life, you have to stay safe while doing so. There are two aspects to running safety: avoiding accidents and, while I regret having to include this in a chapter on safety, avoiding incidents with others who could do you harm. While nothing you do can guarantee safety, following some basic rules, and using common sense, can go a long way toward keeping you safe while running.

I have never completely shaken off an incident that happened quite early in my running career in South Africa. It was early on a Sunday morning, and I was with a large group of runners doing a so-called club run. We were running a circular course used for a popular 32k (20-mile) race, but in the reverse direction. At one point, we passed three runners going the other way, running the course in the direction used for the race. I had met one of them; he was at many of the road races I ran. They were on the opposite side of the road, facing oncoming traffic, as we were, not that there was much traffic early on a Sunday on roads that were beyond built-up suburban areas. A while later, we heard the sirens of emergency vehicles. As we finished our run, word reached us that the three of them had been hit from behind by a car on a sharp bend. The car failed to take the bend, crossed over into the lane for oncoming traffic, left the road entirely, and killed all of them instantly. As I say, they were facing oncoming traffic and did nothing wrong. They were simply in the wrong place at the wrong time.

Then, I recall a young friend who was running to work one morning when he was set upon by four youths who beat him up, leaving him injured, and stole his running shoes. There was nothing else of value to steal. Running, especially on the roads, does carry risks.

From a safety perspective, where is the best place to run? To be honest, the safest place might be indoors, on an indoor track or on a treadmill. Personally, I dislike running around and around on an indoor track and have only done this a few times. I do not enjoy treadmills much either, though I know people who happily do all their running in a gym on a treadmill. I do not own one and do not belong to a gym. I only ever use treadmills in hotel gyms when traveling if the location or weather is not conducive to outdoor running; I never exceed twenty minutes or so on a treadmill. I do, however, have a stationary bicycle at home that I ride when the weather is really bad.

As an outdoor runner, I shall therefore discuss safety while running outdoors. There are basically four places to run: in a park, on the roads, on a track, and on trails. Let us talk about safety considerations for each in turn.

Parks are my favorite places to run when I travel on business. When I am in London, I try to stay near Hyde Park or Kensington Gardens so I can do my daily runs there; in Paris, near the Bois de Bourgogne; in New York, near Central Park; in Sydney, near the Botanical Gardens; and in Hong Kong, near Hong Kong Park, small though it is. In the town where I live, there is a 300-acre park with lawns, forests, and trails that are great for running. Through the summer months, every Tuesday evening, there are cross-country races open to all; I participate as often as I can get there.

Why do I like city parks? Principally because they are free of traffic and therefore safer than the roads, and the air is likely to be cleaner. You will also seldom be alone in a city park, at least in daylight hours, so you are relatively safe from assailants and also likely to be found quickly if you fall or have a medical incident. I would, however, not generally advocate running in a park alone after dark, though many city parks are full of runners and walkers in the early evening hours and are therefore probably as safe as in the daylight.

In large parks, like Central Park, to avoid finding yourself alone stick to the main trails after dark. Many New Yorkers will remember the unfortunate Central Park jogger incident in 1989 when a young woman was attacked at night on a remote trail in the park.[22]

All in all, parks are a great place to run, and in many parks the running surface is grass or dirt and therefore softer than the roads.

Not surprisingly, I do most of my running on the roads, as do the vast majority of runners. This is largely a matter of convenience: you lace up your shoes, step outside, and off you go. I should add that if one participates in road races, I think it is desirable to do at least some of one's training on the same surface to get used to it. The downside to road running is that you share the roads with motor vehicles, with all the inherent dangers that creates. Even if there is a sidewalk to run on, you still have to cross intersections. In my opinion, as a runner for nearly five decades, the dangers have increased over time. For one, in many parts of the world, there is an ever-increasing number of vehicles on the road. Secondly, from my observations, the number of distracted drivers seems to have exploded with the advent of smartphones.

Many of us know someone, or at least know of someone, who has had a bad encounter with a motor vehicle, motorcycle, or perhaps a bicycle. Running on roads undeniably has its hazards, but there are a number of common-sense actions one can take to manage the risks. Let me share some I have learned over the years.

First, follow the rules of the road; these apply to pedestrians as well as cars. Do not run through red lights or stop signs, and cross the road only when it is your turn to do so. Second, plan your route to avoid busy roads if you can. Quiet roads are a lot more pleasant as well as safer. Where possible, choose roads where there is a sidewalk, shoulder, or grass verge so you do not have to run on the actual road surface. If you have to run in the road, run as near to the edge as possible.

Third, run *facing* oncoming traffic. You want to see vehicles approaching you; you don't want them approaching you from behind.

It amazes me how many runners do not face oncoming traffic. Of course, if you are taking part in a road race, you must run on the side of the road you are directed to by race officials, who will have consulted the local police on safety for runners and other road users.

One problem I find with facing oncoming traffic is that too many drivers coming out of side streets only look in one direction for oncoming cars—and not the other way for oncoming runners—before entering the road. If you see a car about to pull out of a side street or driveway across your path, stop and wait, unless you can make eye contact with the driver and they acknowledge your presence and allow you to go by. These situations are dangerous.

Be especially careful on two-lane roads where overtaking is permitted. When a driver is passing another vehicle, all their attention is given to the overtaking maneuver. A vehicle that is overtaking and approaching at speed from behind is especially dangerous for runners. Unfortunately, there are also dangerous drivers who will risk overtaking even when not permitted. You can't see the vehicle coming so you need to be alert and rely on your hearing at all times.

There are, however, important exceptions to the general rule of facing oncoming traffic. In my view, these are situations where you cannot see oncoming cars until the last moment and you cannot get off the road if you have to, perhaps because there is a steep bank right next to the road, trees, or bushes beside the road, or steel barriers. Remember if you cannot see oncoming cars, they cannot see you. You may be able to hear a car (more on that in a moment), but they will not be able to hear you. Situations where you cannot see oncoming cars include when you are going over the crest of a hill or around a blind corner. If you can, move off the road surface to the side in these situations, even if the surface is uneven; walk if necessary. It will be safer for you when a car suddenly appears over the hill or around the bend. If you cannot get off the road, then my advice is to move over, well in advance, to the opposite side of the road with oncoming cars *behind* you, listen for approaching cars, and then move back to the other side when it is safe to do so. Always look out for cyclists when crossing from one side to the other as bicycles are difficult to hear. I have to do this maneuver in a number of spots on some of my regular routes near my home. It is simply a matter that a vehicle behind you that can see you is safer than a vehicle in front of you that cannot see you until the last second.

Fourth, concentrate on what you are doing when you run on public roads. Do not assume that drivers see you and will give you a wide berth; many will, but, as I mentioned, distracted driving is a growing problem. A friend who is a local race director has a music metaphor: "See (C) sharp or be (B) flat." Concentrating is easier when running alone; when running with others and engaging in conversation, we can easily become distracted ourselves, and that is not good for our safety. One needs to focus on the surroundings.

Fifth, wear bright colors so you can be seen. The clothes we wear should be selected to make us easily visible to other road users, not to show off our sense of fashion. I am amazed how many people run in black or very dark colors; even in broad daylight against the backdrop of a dark road surface, runners in dark colors are harder to see. Running at night in black is simply crazy. Road workers and police officers on traffic duty are usually in bright, reflective gear so they can easily be seen. Runners should be no different. You may not find red, pink, orange, or yellow fashionable, but they are great for visibility. Keep the dark outfits for your runs in the park, on the track, or on trails where there are no vehicles. At night, one should not only wear bright clothing—white probably being the best—but reflective gear as well.

Finally, let me make a few remarks about listening to music through ear pieces while running on the roads. I will be quite open about it. I started running long before even the first Walkman was invented, so listening to music while running was not an option. I have always enjoyed listening to the sounds around me, whether that be birds chirping or fellow runners chatting. For me, running alone is a time for contemplation and reflection, so I do not listen to music. The bigger reason is safety. Listening to music is a distraction; it affects concentration, and when you run on the roads, you need to concentrate and use all your available senses to stay safe. Listening to podcasts is out of the question, as far as I am concerned. While driving, I frequently come up behind runners who are wearing ear pieces, running on the wrong side of the road, and totally oblivious to the presence of a vehicle, as they cannot see it or hear it. You have probably experienced the same thing.

At the start of a road race I ran a few years ago, the race officials instructed us to run on the right side of the road. Shortly after the start, a police officer who was following the runners in a car called out over the loudspeaker to a young woman running on the left, telling her to move over to the right. She ignored the instruction, so the officer repeated it. I looked over and saw she was wearing ear pieces and could not even hear a police car loudspeaker right behind her! She had probably also not heard the instructions before the start of the race to run on the right, as she was likely listening to music. Headphones or earbuds are actually not allowed in most road races where I live, but enforcing the rule is pretty much impossible. Let me suggest this: if you must listen to music while running, consider listening through just one ear, like you do when you hold a telephone to your ear, so the other ear can pick up sounds from the environment around you. A better suggestion is to limit listening to music while running to when you run in a park in daylight, where there are no cars around, or perhaps on the track if it is not crowded.

The option to safely listen to music is not the only advantage to running on a track. The surface is normally relatively soft, so it is easier on your joints than roads are. The surface is also even so you are less likely to trip or fall, and of course you do not have to worry about traffic, only staying in a lane free of other runners. Some casual runners do practically all their running on the track. For one, it is easy to know how far you have run; you just have to count the laps and multiply by 400 meters. It is also easy to follow your progress in gaining fitness by measuring your time over a given distance, whether that be one lap, twenty-five laps (10 kilometers), or something in between.

Personally, I find going around and around on a track rather boring, and I only go to the track for speed workouts. At my peak, when training for marathons, I might do that twice a week. Doing speed training on the roads is, to my mind, less desirable, as this type of workout requires concentration, and you do not want to have to worry about traffic when running at speed.

Let me briefly explain what I mean by speed workouts before moving on. For experienced runners who are into racing and want to improve their times, training that involves high-intensity bursts of speed followed by a brief period of recovery is a good way to build aerobic capacity and move up a level. A workout I have often done on the track includes six fast 400 meter runs with 100 meters at a slow jog after each one before starting the next. This form of workout is also called interval training.

One tip about running on tracks: run in the outside lanes as much as possible. Some tracks have a sign asking runners to do that. The reason is that in track races longer than 400 meters, all the competitors use the inside lanes. If casual runners use the outside lanes, it evens up wear on the track. Another tip is to stay in the lane you start in. There is nothing more annoying when you are in the midst of a speed session than to have a slower runner drift across into your lane right in front of you. Stay in your lane. When you stop, look behind you before moving to the inside or outside of the track. I have seen too many collisions on crowded tracks when runners stroll across the lanes without looking back first.

Finally, let me talk about running on trails from a safety point of view. Trail running can be different from running in a park, on roads, or on a track, in that you might be completely alone for quite some time, depending on the location. While you are generally safe from traffic dangers running on trails, in other ways, trail running poses a safety risk and I therefore advocate running together with one or more other runners on trails, if you can. Firstly, a group of two or more runners is less likely to be confronted by someone who presents a risk to their physical safety than a lone runner. I worry particularly when I meet female runners (or walkers) on their own on remote trails. Secondly, if you are injured, others can help you immediately.

If you do run alone, try to use trails frequented by other people to minimize the dangers. Running long distances on remote trails where you don't see anyone is problematic if you become injured. Trails have uneven ground, and some have rocks and roots on which you can trip and fall. I have fallen a number of times running alone on trails but fortunately have not injured myself. I have occasionally come across others on my trail runs who were not so fortunate. More than with other surfaces, it is critical to concentrate on where you plant your foot with every single step when running on trails. One mistake and down you go. This means you have to look down and not ahead; if you wish to admire the view, stop to do so.

Running alone on trails is one time it is probably a good idea to carry a mobile phone—if you are in an area where a call is possible. I have done crazy things like run to the bottom of the Grand Canyon and back to the rim; you certainly cannot make a call from down there, but fortunately you will have company on the more popular trails there if you need help. Carry the phone for emergencies and try to avoid using it to listen to music while running on trails. Enjoy nature and concentrate on what you are doing. Listening to music is a distraction and running on trails requires full concentration.

I do not have a dog but have been asked from time to time for advice about running with dogs. I do not think running on the road with a dog is a great idea because of all the hazards I have mentioned, though people do it. I have even seen people taking part in road races with a dog. I also saw someone once running on a track with a dog, much to the annoyance of the other runners. It is surely a better idea to go to the nearest park and run there with a dog. I sometimes see people running on trails with a dog, which I think is fine if it is allowed at the location; one just needs to be alert to avoid tripping and falling.

To conclude, running is a sport that presents some safety risks; however, it is surely safer than a number of other sports and outdoor activities. As I said at the beginning, following basic rules and using common sense will go a long way in keeping you safe while you run.

Let us now discuss some of the more common injuries that runners experience and how to avoid them.

CHAPTER 7

Running Injuries

I know I am not well qualified to give advice on the subject of running injuries, so I will limit what I have to say. First, I do not have a medical background; second, I am fortunate to have enjoyed a largely injury-free running career so there is not a great deal I can tell you based on personal experience. Some runners, including a few of my running friends, are not as fortunate and, for one or other reason, experience injuries from time to time that force them to take a break. I admire their perseverance; they must love the sport as much as I do.

I might be accused of oversimplifying, but for those of us blessed with good genes who are structurally "normal," I believe the overwhelming majority of running injuries are caused by either overdoing it or, to a lesser extent, footwear issues. If you are cursed with structural problems, such as overpronation, that hamper your running, I urge you to seek professional advice from a specialist who works with runners; you may need shoes specifically designed for runners like you, or perhaps an orthotic, to be able to run comfortably and stay injury free.

Let's talk about so-called overuse injuries, which are especially common early in a runner's career as our bodies adjust to the stresses of running. One of my all-time favorite books on running is *The Complete Book of Running* by James L. Fixx,[23] which I referred to in chapter 5. In a chapter titled "If, Despite Everything, Something Goes Wrong" Fixx describes the following injuries: runner's knee (or chondromalacia), stress fractures, plantar fasciitis, heel spurs, Achilles tendonitis, and shin splints. I have suffered from all of these injuries, mainly early in my career, except for heel spurs and stress fractures, which are more common in female runners than in male runners. Fixx also discusses blisters, muscle soreness, and cramps, which I do not classify as injuries for the purpose of this chapter, unpleasant though they are. Muscle soreness is inevitable after a long training run or hard race, but muscle tears are not common in runners, as long-distance running is a continuous motion without the sudden changes in direction or sharp acceleration that are a part of many sports.

Another of my favorite books is *Lore of Running* by Professor Tim Noakes, first published in 1985.[24] Unlike Jim Fixx, who was a journalist turned runner turned author, Tim Noakes is a medical doctor and specialist in exercise physiology at the University of Cape Town. I still like the first edition, as it is "only" five hundred pages long. Material added in subsequent editions lengthened the book. I remember people calling it the runner's bible when it was published because it is so comprehensive.

A lengthy chapter of the book is devoted to running injuries, perhaps not surprising given the author's background. In it, Noakes lists what he calls "The Ten Laws of Running Injuries." These make for interesting reading. He includes three points in his "laws" that I find particularly pertinent: first, injuries indicate the athlete has reached a "breakdown point"; second, virtually all running injuries can be cured; and third, complete rest is seldom necessary. I shall come back to this last point a little later.

Noakes goes on to discuss a number of common injuries, essentially the same ones as those mentioned by Jim Fixx, their possible causes, and treatment alternatives: As best I can tell, the most common injuries runners experience today are essentially the same as they were decades ago when these books were written.

I should also mention Noakes's "Tenth Law of Running Injuries," which resonated with me. It states, "There is as yet no evidence that running causes osteoarthritis in runners whose knees were normal when they started running."[25] Noakes goes on to say he searched the scientific literature and could not find any evidence that running directly causes osteoarthritis in the knees. In fact, he found evidence suggesting runners were less likely to develop this condition. I should stress, though, that the first edition of this book was published in 1985 and the fourth and most recent edition in 2002.

I have long ago lost count of the number of times I have been asked, "How are your knees after all the years of running?" I reply that they are just fine. I started running in my late twenties with two healthy knees. They remain healthy, they function well, and I do not have knee pain. I have reviewed literature from the last ten years, as a layman, and still cannot find any studies that conclude that running causes osteoarthritis. On the contrary, there are recent studies that seem to confirm what Noakes stated: running is beneficial to the knee joints and can actually reduce the incidence of this condition developing later in life. Genetics is considered the main factor in determining who will develop osteoarthritis. This is true for the hips and other joints as well as for the knees.

As I said earlier, there are many benefits to running; do not be deterred by fear that doing so for years on end will cause the onset of osteoarthritis in the knee or hip joints; the evidence suggests it will not. It certainly has not for me. If, however, you already have osteoarthritis starting in the knees, running may accelerate the deterioration of the cartilage, so consult an exercise physiologist or similar expert if you are considering a running program.

For sure, I know some runners around my age who developed osteoarthritis in the knee and ultimately had a knee replacement. However, I know far more who did not. Whether these runners would have developed knee problems because of their genetics if they had not taken up running in the first place is not something we can ever know. The good news is successful knee replacements can enable people to start running again. I know a number of people who have been able to resume running or other athletic activities without any problems after their rehabilitation following this type of surgery.

I have run for well over forty years and, since my first year of running regularly, have experienced only one injury that stopped me from running for about a week: Achilles tendonitis. This was decades ago so if I had known what I know now and applied ice to the injured tendon several times a day from the outset, I might have been able to continue running, as the injury was not that serious. Back then, the only thing I knew was to rest.

I have had only one other injury after my first year that caused me to seek professional help, and that was a sore hip that was getting worse with every long run, to the point where it really bothered me. I would like to relate the story, as it gave me belief that running injuries are almost always treatable, often without rest, as Tim Noakes suggests in his laws of running injuries.

I was deep into my training for the 90k (56-mile) Comrades Marathon in South Africa and putting in heavy training week after week. The injury to which I refer was undoubtedly an overuse injury, and the Comrades was only a month or so away. I decided to call the go-to guy everyone in my running circle visited when injured and needing help. He told me to come for an appointment wearing my normal street shoes and to bring my running shoes with me. He examined me carefully, focusing on my feet, while having me both walk around the room barefoot and lie down. He then closely examined both pairs of shoes. He immediately observed that the right heel on both pairs was worn down more than the left, something I had never noticed, which he attributed to one leg being ever so slightly longer than the other, neither uncommon nor serious, in his mind. He explained how my anatomy coupled with stepping up my training had likely caused the hip pain and said it was easy to treat. In his opinion, I did not need a permanent orthotic, as I had run for many years by then without serious injuries. Perhaps my running shoes at the time were a contributing factor, as I had never experienced hip pain before, nor have I since, even at times when I have been into heavy training.

I was surprised by what happened next: he picked up a yellow pages directory from a stack next to his desk and, using a pair of scissors, cut a shoe insert about three millimeters thick from pages in the directory. He taped around the edges of the insert and placed it in the heel of my left shoe. He told me to wear it in all footwear—walking around at home, at the office, and while running. He also instructed me to open a flap he had made with tape at the back, remove five pages each day, close the flap, and put it back in my shoe. I should continue doing this until all the pages were gone. Over a period of two to three weeks, I would gradually get back to running without the left heel of my shoe raised to compensate for the injury. He had put it in my street shoe and said I should start using it immediately.

I remember asking him if I should stop running and, if so, for how long. He replied that the whole point of seeing him was to avoid having to stop running when training for an ultramarathon! I asked if I would still feel pain when running, and he said I would probably feel some residual discomfort for a day or so, no more. He was right. I asked if I should come for a follow-up visit, and he said that should not be necessary. I walked from the building where he worked about ten blocks back to my office, in leather-soled shoes on a hard sidewalk. The reduction in the pain level was immediately apparent. The wedge in the left heel had the effect of making the left leg do more of the work, so the right hip would gradually recover. Of course, the imbalance caused by using a shoe insert like this indefinitely might itself lead to an injury, but in the short-term, it allowed my hip to recover while I continued to train.

From conversations with other runners who had consulted this therapist, it seemed he treated most injuries this way, placing an insert in either the front or rear of one shoe, depending on the nature of the injury and whether it was on the left or right side. I relate this story not to suggest you try to self-treat running injuries, but to make the point that it is worth seeking professional advice for injuries that impair your running performance and most certainly for injuries that might stop you from running. As Dr. Noakes stated in his laws, rest may not always be necessary, and something like a temporary orthotic may help. In fact, sometimes simply cutting back on the intensity or distance of one's running may be all it takes.

Let me now talk about starting out as a novice runner and the need to go easy for the first year or so to avoid injury. In fact, I cannot stress enough how important it is for beginners to ease into running and not be too ambitious, regardless of age. The longstanding chairman of the running club in Johannesburg to which I belonged in the 1970s and 1980s wrote this a while ago in the club's newsletter:[26]

> I learnt early on that the SECRET to endurance running is PATIENCE. One has to GRADUALLY build up the stress you put on your body with micro increments. Your body readily adapts to these small increases subconsciously. Big jumps or surprise changes set off negative reactions and you are REWARDED with pain or worse, an INJURY which puts you back four or five places. PATIENCE is the SECRET. Simple as that.

He was fortunate to have a mentor, or informal coach, when he started his successful career as a long-distance runner in the 1970s and, by following sound advice, managed to avoid serious injury.

My first year was another story, and I now know why. I was twenty-seven, enthusiastic, and lacking in patience. I ran too much and too hard before my body had adapted to the stresses of running regularly. Adaptation takes time at a young age and longer if one is older. I was running 15 to 20 miles (20 to 30 kilometers) a week from the start and ran my first race, a 24k, only ten weeks after my first run. Three weeks later, as I describe in chapter 1, I ran a marathon in just under four hours! Was I crazy? After both of these races, my left knee was pretty sore for a few days, but fortunately the injury was not serious. Over the following three months, I did a number of shorter races and developed plantar fasciitis, which stopped me running more than a light jog for more than a month. I am convinced this injury was caused by simply pushing the limits at such an early stage of my running career.

Once I was able to resume regular training, I started upping the distance, as I was determined to run the 90k Comrades Marathon at the end of May 1975, barely a year after I started running. To enter, I needed to run another marathon, as the time for my first one was not good enough to qualify. I soon picked up another injury, known as Morton's neuroma, which is a painful condition that affects the ball of the foot. It involves a thickening of tissue around a nerve leading to the toes and feels like there is a small stone in the shoe. I put up with the pain until I had run the marathon, finishing in just under three and a half hours and qualifying for the Comrades, but by the end of the race, it was so sore I had to stop running for three weeks.

Then, guess what I did over the next two months after I was able to resume running: two ultramarathons in the 50k to 60k range! Between the two events, I developed pain in my right knee, which was quite sharp at times, and after the second ultramarathon, I was forced to stop running. I visited a physical therapist who diagnosed the injury as chondromalacia, colloquially known as "runner's knee," as the injury is so common among runners. It is a classic overuse injury, a condition where the cartilage on the undersurface of the kneecap deteriorates. It is different from arthritis and is generally treatable. The therapist treated the injury with ultrasound and gave me exercises to do. This drastically limited my training in the weeks leading up to the Comrades Marathon, but I was determined to run it. I endured some knee pain in the latter stages of the race but was able to continue and earn my medal. I then took a few weeks off from running and have not been troubled by this injury again, but I learned my lesson the painful way. If you are thinking of starting to run regularly, which is what this book is about, do not try crazy things like I did in the first year.

Over the next few years, I sometimes developed shin splints when I stepped up my training, but the pain never reached a level that I was forced to stop running, and after a couple of weeks or so, it subsided. This is simply another example of a common overuse injury when running too much without building up gradually.

In the years since, the only injuries I have suffered are occasional episodes of Achilles tendonitis, which could be because the shoes I was wearing at the time were not up to the task, but I have been able to keep running by icing the injury several times a day, while easing back on both distance and speed. Occasionally I have suffered minor knee pain but nothing chronic and nothing that has stopped me running. I find that stretching helps both the knees and Achilles tendons, areas of the body where running injuries are particularly common. Running sensibly and patiently, coupled with stretching, has allowed me to run many years now without an injury at all. There is plenty you can read elsewhere about how—and how not—to stretch, so I will not go into detail on a subject about which I am not qualified to advise. Working with a trainer to develop a stretching routine is something to consider. Suffice it to say, regular stretching is important for avoiding injury and you need to find out what works for you, which I have done over the years.

To emphasize my point about building up gradually, let me give you another example of the consequences of overambition in the infancy of a running career, but this time with a female runner. Over the two year period when I was sixty-eight and sixty-nine years old, I entered very few races, partly because age-group awards are almost always in ten-year categories, and as you get close to the end of a decade, you cannot compete with those just entering the decade. I continued to run most days; I simply cut back on going to races. The second, and perhaps more important, reason is that I wanted to be "race fresh" when I turned seventy, full of enthusiasm to race again and competitive on my local running scene against other seventy-year-olds.

Three months before I turned seventy, as I started to build up to get myself ready to race again, I entered a popular local half-marathon that I have done many times, my first race in about six months, aiming to run it at about 9 minutes a mile (5 minutes 40 seconds per kilometer). As the field started to thin out as we neared the one-mile mark, a young lady who had been running just behind my right shoulder for a couple of minutes said, "We seem to be running at the same pace."

"Yes," I replied, "around nine minutes a mile."

Shortly after that, we passed the first marker in exactly nine minutes, which I confirmed to her after looking at my watch. "That is too fast for me," she said. "I was aiming for around nine and a half. This is my first half-marathon."

I did not comment; we all have to find our own pace in a race. Nevertheless, she stayed with me as I continued at this pace, and in due course, I learned this was not only her first half-marathon, but it was her first road race over any distance! Remember my first race was a 25k. Sound familiar? I later learned she was the same age as I was when I ran that first race. She stuck with me all the way, somewhat to my surprise, and as we rounded the last corner and saw the finish line about a minute away, I yelled, "If we sprint, we can break two hours!" which we did with seconds to spare. She said she would have been happy with two and half hours. What she was really hoping for, I do not know.

As we parted, I told her about another half-marathon in the area in four weeks that I planned to run. I told her it was a tougher course than the one we just finished, which had hardly a hill. She said she would like to do it and hoped to see me there. This one had a smaller field, and we found each other at the start and set out together. After all, for me, this was just part of my buildup for when I turned seventy; the time did not matter, and I had no hope of winning an award. I said I was happy to again run at around a nine-minute pace if that suited her. I wish I had enjoyed the company of an experienced runner to guide me in my first year; in fact, what I had was a few running friends pushing me to do too much.

In the latter stages, she struggled with the hills, but I held back and ran with her, finishing in a few minutes over two hours, not that I minded. She ran the race injury free; however, she told me she had suffered from a strained right hip flexor after the first race, which hampered her training during the month in between. The injury recurred following the second one. Once she was over that, she found a half-marathon about an hour away that I did not know about and suggested we both run it, which I said I would consider. Training for it, however, she developed pain in the outside of the left knee that stopped her running and prevented her from doing it.

When she was back in training a few weeks later, we ran a 15k together slowly and then a fairly tough half-marathon in 1 hour, 56 minutes. This was my first race after turning seventy, and the time was good enough to win the age-group award. After that run, which she found quite comfortable, I could see her ambition growing. A mere two weeks later, she insisted on joining me at another half-marathon with lots of hills—a popular one where I had won the age division prize in the year that I turned sixty. I wanted to repeat that ten years later. At the start, she asked me to help her to break 1 hour 50 minutes. I thought that was way too ambitious but let her set the pace. In the latter stages, I dropped back but still finished under her target and won the age-group award easily. I was a minute or so behind her. Two days later, she sent me a message that she had experienced severe Achilles tendonitis during a training run on a trail and had to walk back to her car. Rest and multiple rounds of ultrasound treatment put paid to her plans to run several races, including a first marathon—on a mountainous trail course—an event I had tried unsuccessfully to dissuade her from entering.

When she recovered from that, once again she tried to build up too quickly, and a groin injury and then a strained hamstring followed. Much like me in my first year of running, she chose to look past the injuries and set her sights on running a fifty-mile (80 km) trail race around the anniversary of her first half-marathon. I did not think this was a good idea at all—I knew all about running the Comrades Marathon only a year after first lacing up a pair of running shoes—but I knew I would be wasting my time trying to talk her out of it. I remembered my younger self all too well!

The injuries hampered her training but were not serious enough to stop her running; the problem was she did not reduce the weekly distance she was running, which one should do when working through an injury. Meanwhile, I was continuing my unbroken streak of winning age-group awards and was happy to have someone to train with from time to time, who was willing to do runs of more than an hour. One weekend, we did a long training run together, on trails in a nature reserve. I was not having a particularly good day and was holding her back much of the time; however, late in the run, she slowed down dramatically and complained of intense pain in her foot. An X-ray showed this to be a stress fracture of the second metatarsal bone, a common overuse injury, especially in women runners. I suspect that the groin or hamstring injury was causing her to favor one side of her body, and that put added strain on the foot.

There were four months left before the fifty-mile trail race at that point. This new injury put her out of action for two months. By then, she had hired a "coach," an accomplished long-distance trail runner who lived in another part of the country whose coaching services she received remotely. She told me she had asked the coach, with whom she had shared the X-ray, whether she could still run the fifty-miler in spite of the stress fracture and that he replied he saw "no reason" why she could not. I was astounded and told her so. A layoff of two months is almost like starting from scratch in terms of loss of fitness, and the amount of work one needs to put in to prepare for a race of that distance cannot be done in the remaining two months; further injuries would surely follow were one to try. The coach's advice was what she wanted to hear; mine wasn't. I knew the feeling.

It turned out the coach was wrong, and she was unable to do the race. Like me, however, in time, she overcame the spate of injuries she endured in the first year caused by not giving the body time to adjust to the stresses of running. The following year she ran two 50-kilometer trail races only weeks apart and finished with decent times in both.

The question is why put yourself through an experience like this? My reason for giving these two quite similar examples, my own experience and that of a novice female runner I met by chance, is to illustrate the folly of not building up gradually as one gets into running. This is the single most important piece of advice I can give to a beginning runner, regardless of age.

Moving on, as I said at the beginning of this chapter, issues with running shoes are perhaps the second most common cause of injury, and I have devoted several pages to a discussion of footwear in the next chapter; this is, quite literally, where "the rubber hits the road."

In conclusion, using common sense, curbing ambition, listening to one's body, and wearing the right shoes will allow most of us to enjoy our running largely injury-free.

CHAPTER 8

Running Shoes and Other Gear

The only sport I can think of that requires less equipment than running is swimming. However, swimming requires access to a swimming pool, or at least some sort of body of water, whereas you can run practically anywhere there is a suitable surface. To run, all you need is the right clothing for the conditions and a pair of running shoes. This makes running an ideal sport for when you travel, one of many benefits I have found as a runner. In fact, I often wear my running shoes on the way to my destination, whether driving or flying.

By far, the most important equipment you need to buy is a pair of shoes, so let's talk about those first. Running shoes have come a long way over the past forty years or so. For running on the roads, there are hundreds of makes and models from which to choose, with a wide range of prices. This is a far cry from the few models that existed when I started running in the mid-1970s. If you look at the cover of the best-selling 1977 book by Jim Fixx to which I referred earlier, *The Complete Book of Running*, there is a photo of the author's muscular legs in a simple red pair of shoes with a thin sole. I started running in exactly the same model of shoes, though mine were blue. The upper part of the shoe does not look much different today, but you will see there was no midsole at all back then, no cushioning whatsoever, and the shoes did not provide any stability for runners who needed it. Basically, you had a nylon upper glued to a hard rubber sole.

Given the myriad of makes and models of shoes now available, a beginner would be well advised to consult a running shoe specialist before starting out. An expert can discuss the pros and cons of various models, let you try on a few, watch you run a few steps in the store, and get you started in a pair of shoes that is right for you. Once you have some experience, you can probably figure out what to buy by reading about the features of various models online or in a running magazine, if you prefer.

Let me make two further points regarding running shoes. Unlike a brand-new pair of leather shoes, running shoes should feel totally comfortable the moment you put them on in the store. If they do not, try a different size (length or width) or a different model. The second thing to note is that one's feet swell when one runs, so the shoe should be ever so slightly loose when you put them on. If they are tight when your feet are cold, you might have problems when you run in them. I generally go for one size bigger in running shoes compared to everyday shoes, but that depends on the make and model, as I find running shoe sizing lacks consistency across brands.

Most of the time, I actually have four pairs of running shoes in use. Two are for everyday training on the road, and are at different points in their life cycle so, when I have to buy new shoes, I can alternate the new ones with a pair that is worn in. I am not sure this is entirely necessary, but I have long followed this practice. I usually run in one pair for a few days and then switch to the other pair. My two pairs are similar in style but normally not identical models. The third pair is what are sometimes called "racing flats," a pair that weighs slightly less, which I use only for races and speed workouts on the track. I think the advantage in terms of less weight, and therefore more speed, is essentially nonexistent for a runner like me; it is more a psychological lift I hope to get from going to the start line in my racing shoes.

The fourth pair are trail-running shoes, which you will not need if you plan to run only on roads. I like to run on trails as well as on the road, and the tread of trail shoes gives one better traction on loose surfaces. I also find they are better for running on grass in parks. I often use them for hiking on trails too.

As I mentioned in the last chapter, I suspect the second most common cause of injury, after overuse, is footwear. From my years of running, I would suggest there are three shoe-related factors that can lead to injury. The first is the shoes are new and inflexible, the second is the type of shoe is not suitable for your biomechanics, and the third is the shoes are too worn and not providing the level of support that you need.

Let's take these one at a time. Years ago, when I started running in a new pair of shoes, I sometimes experienced aches and pains, though nothing serious, until the shoes were worn in. I remember this happening even with the same brand and model of shoe I had been running in for months, just with a new pair. Runners have told me of going to run a marathon in a brand-new pair of shoes, again the same make and model as they normally wear, and coming away with an injury. Never, never do that! I put this down to the lack of flexibility in a new pair of shoes. Take a running shoe you have been wearing for some time and flex it; then do the same with a new or almost-new running shoe and notice the difference. Whatever the manufacturer may say, I find that running shoes are somewhat stiff when they are new.

Maybe I am overcautious, but here is what I do whenever I buy a new pair of running shoes:

1. I walk around the house in them for a week or so. They become my house shoes, only to be worn indoors.
2. Then I use them as walking shoes for a few weeks, wearing them to the grocery store, to buy gas, or when taking a walk on a trail.
3. Only after that do I start running in the new shoes, starting with short runs and gradually moving up to longer distances.
4. I alternate the new shoes and another pair I have been using for a while that are worn in.

Since adopting this approach, I have not had any problems with new shoes. When I find shoes I like, I try to buy at least two more pairs immediately, as the shoe companies continually tweak their product lineup, and I have found on occasion that I do not like the updated model as much as the one I have been wearing.

As I say, I have two pairs of training shoes in use at any given time, usually different models. That way, if one of the models is discontinued, there is another pair of shoes that I am used to that is likely available while I look for a replacement for the discontinued model.

The second category of footwear-related injury is the type of shoe. There are hundreds of makes and models of running shoes designed for the road (fewer for trails or track), and most fall into one of two principal categories: neutral or motion control. Motion-control shoes are intended for runners who overpronate when they run— this means they roll the foot inward to a greater degree than most of us after striking the ground. When starting out as a novice runner, it is a good idea to see a running shoe specialist who can watch you run a few strides, assess whether you need motion-control shoes, and make recommendations.

I am well suited to neutral running shoes, and that is what I buy. Occasionally, however, I have tried a new model and, even after following my routine to break in the shoes, have developed pain while running, usually knee pain. I then go back to my old shoes and generally find the pain is not there. If I still have pain after running a few times in the new shoes, either while running or afterward, I conclude the shoes are simply not right for me and give them away or use them as walking shoes. There is no point in struggling in shoes that cause discomfort. Try a different model. Running is only fun if the shoes are right for you.

One other point about the type of shoe: in his fascinating and bestselling 2009 book, *Born to Run*,[27] Christopher McDougall discusses the highly cushioned shoes that were first developed in the 1970s that allow one to extend the stride and strike the ground with the heel instead of the ball of the foot. He talks about how this can lead to injuries that one would not otherwise suffer. Try landing on your heel running barefoot—you simply cannot, one needs a well-cushioned shoe to do so. McDougall's point is that landing on the heel is not natural. We were not built to run like that, and we run the risk of injury by doing so.

I do not have an opinion on what McDougall says, as I have never been a heel striker. The shoes that were available when I started lacked a cushioned midsole and did not allow one to run any other way than one would barefoot. Because I started with simple shoes and got used to them, I have always stuck with shoes that provide only moderate cushioning. They are also, by the way, generally cheaper. Is this a reason why I have suffered so few injuries? I cannot say for sure, but I imagine McDougall might argue not being a heel striker helps. I have little doubt that one is less likely to become injured if one runs the way one would run barefoot, with an upright torso over the feet. Naturally one has to adjust this posture when running uphill or downhill, but in the same way as one would without shoes at all.

Lastly, let's talk about wear and tear. I find my running shoes are usually good for about 400 to 500 miles, say 600 to 800 kilometers. How long depends on factors such as the weight of the runner, the efficiency of their running style, and the surface on which they do most of their running. When you have finished with a pair of shoes, be sure to take them to an athletic shoe store that receives old shoes for recycling—you do not want shoes to end up in a landfill.

Many of us tend to flog a pair of shoes we really like to death, but this is not a good idea. When they are worn out, stop using them before they lead to injury.

There are three basic parts to a running shoe, the upper, midsole, and outer sole. Uppers are made from nylon or similar fabric and will usually outlast the rest of the shoe. The midsole is the layer of cushioning below the upper, and the outer sole is the hard sole that makes contact with the running surface.

The outer sole will start to wear from the day you start running in a new pair of shoes, especially at the heel. Whether this wear can lead to injury over time is disputed. Some argue you are simply wearing down the heel to the point that your running style desired in the first place. I am not sure I buy that; nevertheless, by the time the outer sole is completely worn down at the heel (or the toe) on one or both shoes, I would say it is time to toss the shoes out if you have not already done so. At that point, mine often become gardening shoes for a while until they completely fall apart.

By then, if not before, the midsole is probably no longer doing its job. I suspect most injuries resulting from worn shoes are because the midsole has compacted to the point where it is ineffective. Over time, this reduces the cushioning effect. You can test the cushioning by taking out the removable inner sole from the shoe and then pressing down from inside the shoe with your fingers to test the sponginess of the midsole. It is worth doing this after you have had a pair of shoes for a while, even if the outer sole still looks OK.

The point is running shoes are the only piece of equipment that is relatively expensive in this sport; it is worth making the investment in new shoes before they become too worn, so you can continue to enjoy your running without courting injury.

Let's turn to running clothing; I hardly need to tell you that synthetic fibers are far more breathable than natural fibers, though I hate to say this when I consider the well-being of the planet. (If we run to our destination instead of taking a car, we can, of course, contribute to sustainability that way.) I still see a lot of people running on the roads in cotton T-shirts, and if they have been running for any length of time, the shirt is usually damp and looks uncomfortable. I know this only too well, as I ran mostly in cotton tops until around 2000, when so-called technical T-shirts started to become more commonplace. These fabrics are better at allowing sweat to evaporate so you feel more comfortable as you run, especially in hot weather.

On the subject of running to your destination, I might mention that I have been fortunate in being able to run between my home and my place of work for much of my career. I worked in office buildings that had showers and lockers while living in Johannesburg, London, and here in Connecticut, and was able to do much of my weekday running during those years as my commute. I would try to do this twice a week when training for a marathon, running for up to ten miles (16k) each way. I now work from home and have flexibility as to when to go out for a run.

Many runners buy synthetic designer tops that look great. I may be considered cheap, but I also think about all the oil that goes into making these garments, so I mostly wear the T-shirts I receive by entering races, at least for training. Some are cotton, some are synthetic. I have many of these from all the years of running races. I pick the shirts with some thought when I travel; race T-shirts can be a conversation piece. Try wearing your Boston Marathon T-shirt when you run in Bangkok or vice versa. It will draw attention.

The clothing one wears is naturally greatly influenced by the weather. Where I started running in South Africa, summers are warm but seldom excessively hot, and winters are mild. Basically, you run in the same clothes year-round as one can do in, say, the southern part of the United States. In Connecticut, where I live now, and Europe, where I lived previously, this is not the case. The question then is are you a "fair-weather runner" or an "all-weather runner"? I am firmly in the latter camp, but it seems to me many people in Connecticut must be in the former, as I see far fewer people running outdoors in the winter, and there are fewer entrants at winter races. Perhaps the rest head for the gym and run on a treadmill.

Let's consider clothing for running in cold weather. Above the waist, I move from synthetic short-sleeve T-shirts or singlets to long-sleeved T-shirts and add a second layer, usually cotton, as the temperature drops and a third layer when it is really cold. I find it better to simply add layers rather than wearing heavy winter clothing that does not breathe well and may lead to overheating. I have always preferred to feel a bit cold for the first ten minutes rather than too hot for the next fifty minutes of a one-hour run. Others prefer winter jackets designed for cold-weather running.

You will, however, definitely need a windbreaker for days when the wind howls, as well as a waterproof top if you plan to run when it rains. Above all, clothing should always be light in color so you are easily visible, if you run on the roads.

I run in shorts down to about 40°F (5C). Below that temperature, I wear tights underneath my running shorts to keep my legs warm. Where I live, this is the case for about four months of the year on most days, especially if I run early in the day. My practice for wearing gloves is much the same; I generally start my run wearing gloves if it is below that temperature and then take them off during the run and tuck them into my clothing if my hands become too warm.

Many people run in a cap or woolen hat in cold weather. I have a fairly full head of hair and find my head does not feel the cold much; with me, it is only my ears that get cold, so I prefer to cover them in cold weather with a band or earmuffs. As far as socks go, I like to wear thin socks in the warmer months and thicker socks when the weather turns cold but socks are largely a matter of personal preference (especially the color).

As you read the first paragraph of this chapter, you may have thought I was forgetting one important piece of equipment, and you would be right—a watch. For most of the years I have been running, I have worn a simple digital watch with a stopwatch function. When running a new route away from home, I would estimate the distance I had run from the time I spent running and how hard I was running and enter that estimate in my running diary. With the arrival of GPS watches that connect with satellites, estimation is no longer necessary, as the watch gives you the exact distance. There is an enormous range in the prices of these watches. I have a fairly inexpensive one, yet it provides all kinds of information besides the distance I have run: it tells me my heart rate, the speed I am running at any given moment, the time for every mile or kilometer I run, my average speed, the approximate number of calories burned, and even the time of day. You can download this data to another device if you wish.

I mentioned my running diary. I am somewhat obsessed with running statistics and have recorded the distance I have run, and where I ran, since I started running decades ago. I used to do this in a little book but now use a simple spreadsheet. With GPS watches, it is now very easy to store this information if one desires to keep a log. It is certainly not essential to keep records like I do—regular exercise is all that matters.

Finally, and arguably the most important item in terms of gear, is identification, with your name, address, and a telephone number where someone who knows you can be contacted. The more sophisticated watches can store this information in a way that it can be easily accessed. Mine does not, so I run with a tag with this information attached to the watch strap, easy for someone to locate. I urge you to always run with some form of ID on you, even when running with others. ID is important if you enter races, when you will probably run harder than you do during your daily routine.

As I keep saying, however, you do not need to enter races to enjoy the many health benefits of running described earlier in this book, but many runners like to, as do I, so let us now explore the race scene, starting with the 5k and working up to the marathon and beyond. I might add that if you have no interest in finding out more about this subject, you can always skip the next four chapters and go to chapter 13, where I talk about the impact of aging on runners.

I take part in trail, cross-country and road races.
This course is one of my favorite trail races

Chapter 9

An Introduction to the Racing Scene

T his chapter is an introduction to the racing scene, rather than an introduction to racing as such, for those interested in participating in organized running events. Races can be a lot of fun, even for the overwhelming majority of runners who do not aspire to win trophies. The most popular race distances are 5 kilometers, 10 kilometers, and the half-marathon, so these are the ones I shall discuss in this chapter. Races of these distances take place in parks and on trails, but by far, the majority are on roads. Sometimes the roads are closed to traffic, especially for big events, but usually they are not, so one needs to be vigilant at all times.

The 5k

I can say without much hesitation that the 5k race—a little over three miles—is by far the most popular road race distance in the United States, where I live. It is also a common cross-country race distance. It is impossible to know how many are held in a given year, but it has to be thousands. Some are one-off charity fundraisers; others are staged in conjunction with marathons, half-marathons, and even 10k races, where they significantly boost the number of entrants by attracting runners not interested in the longer distances. Every year on US Thanksgiving Day, communities across the country stage a "Turkey Trot," and most of these are 5k. I know a couple of people who run one race a year and that is a Turkey Trot every November.

Living in Europe for many years, I found there were more 10k races than 5k; the same is true in South Africa, where I started my running career. As a result, I never got into running the 5k very much myself. I am also not very good at this distance. To do well at 5k, you need the DNA of a middle-distance runner—after all, 5k on the road is 5,000 meters on the track, one of the classic middle-distance track events. As I noted earlier, I have the DNA of a sprinter, with fast-twitch muscle fibers, and have never been remotely competitive over 5k.

Although I personally prefer longer distances, I really believe this is where a novice to the racing scene should start. You do not need months of training to try a 5k race. In my view, a couple of months of running distances up to 5k around three or four times a week is all you need, as long as you take it relatively easy on race day; do not get carried away with enthusiasm and run the risk of picking up an injury.

The 5k distance often attract large numbers of noncompetitive runners and can be fun, social outings that do not take long to complete. The best runners can complete a 5k in less than fifteen minutes, but the nice thing is even the most social of runners will finish in not much more than half an hour. In fact, some 5k races encourage entries from those who wish to walk the course rather than run, and I do not mean race walkers but rather those whose preferred form of exercise is recreational walking. While you might find local 5k races in parks and on trails, consider starting out running them on the roads, as road courses are generally easier. Leave the trails until you are more experienced.

You may wish to start participating in 5k races with a view to building up to longer distances—10k, half-marathon, and perhaps beyond, if you have the desire. Just take your time and get a few 5k races under your belt first. However, many runners enjoy the 5k distance and have no ambition to take part in races beyond that. They might go a little further in a training run, but when it comes to entering races, 5k it is—and there's nothing wrong with that at all. If what you want out of running is to gain the health benefits I discussed earlier and keep the routine going year in and year out, there is no need to race longer distances. There are so many 5k races in a year in many parts of the world that you will have plenty of opportunities to lace up and head to the start line.

The 10k

Yes, you may find some 5-mile or 8k events on the local race calendar, but the next classic distance beyond the 5k is double that distance, the 10k, equivalent to the longest classic track race, the 10,000 meters. As I previously mentioned, in the United States this distance is not as popular as the 5k; nevertheless, all over the world there are many 10k races around, some held in conjunction with longer events and others as standalone races.

If you want to step up from running a 5k race, this is generally what you will be looking at doing—running double the distance is a very different undertaking. Firstly, it is not practical to walk the distance, a little over six miles, and expect the race staff to still be there when you finish. Sure, you can walk part of it, but 10k races are not for walkers. Secondly, you need to train for longer and run further in order to be prepared. For most runners, I would advise not moving up to run the 10k until you are able to run a 5k in under 30 minutes. You also need to build more stamina by putting in training runs of up to an hour. The distance covered is less important than being on your feet running for an hour. When you can run with reasonable comfort for that length of time, you should be ready to tackle a 10k. Finishing a 10k for the first time can be quite a thrill.

I have always enjoyed this distance even though I was, for most of my running career, more competitive over longer distances. It is said that you can multiply your 10k time by five to obtain an estimate of the time in which you are capable of running a marathon. So, if you run a 10k in an hour you should be able to run a marathon in five hours. In my case, however, five times my best 10k is twenty-three minutes slower than my best marathon time. If this says anything, it is that I was not very good at the 10k even at my peak; I'm better at marathons, as I know all too well.

Surprisingly, the first time I won anything in my many years of running was at a 10k race in Trier, Germany, near where I was living at the time, shortly after I turned fifty. I drove to the race with a friend and ran it, and then the two of us drove home. A week later, the race director sent me my medal in the mail for coming third in the 50–59 years category. Having never won an award in over twenty years of running, I never gave a thought to stay for the prize-giving! As I discuss in chapter 13, however, the competition becomes less intense with every decade that passes once you turn fifty. It is not that my running had improved or that I had stepped up my training, there was simply less competition once I turned fifty, as I would continue to find out in subsequent years.

I ran many 10k races in Europe during that period and then moved to London, where I found plenty of opportunities to run this distance. On the first weekend of every month, there was a 10k race inside Regent's Park, which I did many times. I ran 10k races in other parks around London, as well as on the road, including a big one that crossed the famous Tower Bridge.

I have a favorite 10k near where I live now in Connecticut. This race is held every year in May, on Mother's Day, just as the weather is starting to turn warmer in southern New England. For many years, it was basically a circular course, starting and finishing at a beach on Long Island Sound, with a few hills but quite fast. I have done it many times over the past twenty years, only missing out occasionally. I am not sure if it has to do with one's mindset, but I have never had a bad run on this course and, by my standards, have had a number of pretty good runs.

The year I turned sixty I ran it in forty-two minutes and broke the age-group record. The following year I beat my own record with a time a little under forty-two minutes. That record stood until the year I turned seventy when a guy who had just entered the decade

broke it. I went up and congratulated him after the race. As conso-
lation, however, I set a new seventy age-group record that day of
forty-seven minutes. The following year, they changed the course to
a more scenic out-and-back-type course with a loop around a park at
the halfway mark, so those "old course" records remain.

A nice thing about running 10k races is that they are over in an
hour or less for most of us (half an hour if you are world class.) So,
once you have done a few 5k races, you might consider stepping up
your distance in training and try a 10k. I doubt you will regret it.

The Half-Marathon

The first half-marathon I ran was in November 1979, roughly five
years after I started running regularly. It was the first time I had heard
of a half-marathon. I was living in Johannesburg, South Africa, and the
local running club that organized the race said they got the idea from
the United States, where the distance was growing in popularity. Up
to that time, there were few road races between 15k and 30k, or say 10
and 20 miles, so the half-marathon distance of 21.1 kilometers or 13.1
miles filled a gap. Its popularity has grown over the years to the point
where some believe it is the second most popular road race distance
after the 5k. The dedicated half-marathon website *halfmarathon.net*
lists well over 2,000 half-marathons in the United States alone; no
doubt there are many others not listed on this site, and I would not
be surprised if there have been years with over 3,000 half-marathons
held in the United States, so popular has the distance become.

Most are on the roads, but the list on this site includes a fair
number of half-marathons on trails. I have only done one and found
it quite a challenge. While I love running and racing on trails, I find
distances beyond 10k hard work mentally, as trail running requires
great concentration. If, however, you get into half-marathons and
like the distance, running some of them on trails can provide variety.

The history of the marathon is well documented, but for the
half-marathon, I have not been able to find much history. According

to the website worldathletics.org, the first men's "world's best" time recorded by the International Association of Athletics Federations (IAAF) "was Ron Hill's 1:05:44 clocking in Freckleton, England in 1965."[28] So we know for sure the half-marathon was run back in 1965. From my informal inquiries, however, it seems the half-marathon only became a regular distance on the road-running circuit in the United States in the second half of the 1970s, with the boom in recreational running that I described earlier. Of the many half-marathons, I have run while living in Connecticut, the one that goes back the furthest changed from a marathon to a half-marathon event in 1978. Today there are twenty to twenty-five half-marathons every year in Connecticut and many of them draw large numbers.

Much of this popularity is due to the fact that the amount of training required to finish a half-marathon in good shape is so much less than for a marathon. While I do not advocate running a marathon in the first year after starting a running program, most runners with the desire can build up to doing a half-marathon if all goes well that first year. Ideally, one should be up to doing 20 to 25 miles or 30 to 40 kilometers a week for a number of weeks before tackling a half-marathon, with several long runs of around 10 miles, or 16 kilometers. This is much more manageable than the training required for a marathon, and I have grown to love the event over the years.

While not part of the Olympics or World Athletics Championships, an IAAF World Half Marathon Championship was established in 1992. The one-hour mark was broken for the first time by the great Kenyan runner Moses Tanui, who clocked 59:47 in Milan in 1993. As of the time of writing, the men's record is down to 57 minutes, and the women's record is 1 hour 4 minutes.

The popularity of the event is well illustrated by one of Connecticut's most popular events, a 20k called the New Haven Road Race, which started in 1977. I have run it many times. For years, this race has doubled as the US 20k championships. In 2015, I received a questionnaire asking my opinion, as a finisher, regarding the idea of adding a half-marathon alternative to the 20k distance. For me, the New Haven Road Race was always a 20k event and should stay that way; however, I had little doubt that the majority would support adding the half-marathon. That is what happened the following year.

Looking at the number of finishers in recent years, I do not see evidence that adding a half-marathon distance attracted new entrants, but the greater popularity of the additional 1.1 kilometers is stunning. In 2015, there were 1,844 finishers for the 20k race. In 2016, the first year with the half-marathon alternative, it had 1,146 finishers while the 20k dropped to 669 finishers. That disparity has continued. Clearly, the half-marathon is a big deal for many runners.

I mentioned that the 5k is said to be the most popular distance of all. The New Haven Road Race bears this out. For many years, they have offered a 5k race as well, which starts shortly after the 20k and half-marathon (which start together and are on the same course until around the 19k mark.) In 2015, the 5k had 3,062 finishers, more than 50 percent higher than the 20k. In the years since, the number of 5k finishers has been significantly higher than that of the two longer events combined. Such is the popularity of the 5k.

New York Road Runners, one of the largest running clubs in the world, which organizes the New York City Marathon, well understands the popularity of the half-marathon and for years has presented a series of five half-marathons, one in each of the five New York boroughs. The Manhattan Half Marathon, which I have run several times, loops inside Central Park; the others are on the road.

As best I can tell, there are not nearly as many city half-marathons as there are city marathons; however, in 2006, this club introduced one: the New York City Half Marathon, a large-scale event with prize money to attract top athletes. I participated in the first event, which started in Central Park and finished at Battery Park at the southern tip of Manhattan. In recent years, however, it has started at Prospect Park in Brooklyn, crossing the East River into Manhattan, to finish in Central Park. It attracts a large field.

I said I have a favorite 10k. I also have a favorite half-marathon. It is one I did a number of times in Luxembourg in the 1990s while living in that part of Europe—the *Route du Vin Semimarathon.* The event goes back to 1962, long before the half-marathon existed as a road race distance for the masses, and was apparently slightly shorter in the earlier years. It has been designated as a half-marathon since the late 1970s and followed, from the beginning, a point-to-point route along the Moselle River in the beautiful wine country that straddles both sides of the river along the Germany–Luxembourg border. It was the only large-scale road-running event in the country back then (the Luxembourg Marathon began in 2006). The race started in the town of Remich and finished in the small town of Grevenmacher, along the river to the north. The course lacked any serious hills and, because it followed the meandering river downstream in the direction of its meeting with the Rhine, was very fast. I loved the course and recorded some good times. I last ran it in 1998. Two years later, the course was changed to an out-and-back course, starting and finishing in Remich, so it could qualify for half-marathon records. The course I ran, being a slightly downhill course, did not count for records, not that I, or most of the large field, ever cared. What I learned running this event is that a road race on a scenic course, even without many spectators, can be very uplifting. I found it a joy to run, and I am sure it still is.

Other Distances

What I find unfortunate, especially for runners who want to train for a marathon, is how few races there are between the half-marathon distance and the marathon. Running races of, say, 30 kilometers or 20 miles is, in my experience, of immense value in training for a marathon. The problem is there are not many around, which is a pity—more on this in the next chapter.

CHAPTER 10

The Marathon

I imagine most people who have no interest in distance running have heard of something called the marathon, if only because they have a friend who runs them, they live in a city where roads are closed off for hours and hours one day every year for runners, or they have watched the Summer Olympic Games and seen the marathon event, which, for men, is traditionally held on the day of the closing ceremony and for women earlier in the second week. Some years ago, I attended a three-week course at a business school where we had a visiting professor from Ohio who ran every day and even ran a local half-marathon one weekend during the course. I remember him telling the class he had done one marathon in his long running career and suggested that "every runner should do one marathon." I am not sure running a marathon is essential for anyone, but as a marathon runner myself, I can understand where he was coming from. I have met many runners over the years who have run just one marathon. After all, it is the classic distance in the sport of road running.

I have run the standard marathon distance seventy-six times on three continents over a forty-year period. In 1988, a peak year for me, I ran seven of them, plus four ultramarathons. I therefore have a good deal of experience with training for one, with how the body adapts as you do so, and with what happens physiologically and psychologically during a marathon. I shall try to share some of what I have learned in this chapter in case you consider stepping it up and running your first marathon one day.

Let's first briefly explore the history of the marathon and why the distance is 42.195 kilometers, equivalent to 26 miles and 385 yards.[29]

It started with the advent of the modern Olympic Games in 1896, held in Athens. According to Greek folklore, a messenger named Philippides ran from a battlefield at the town of Marathon to Athens to announce that the heavily outnumbered Greek army had defeated Persian invaders. He is said to have collapsed and died immediately after making the announcement. The battle took place in 490 BC. There is doubt about the historical accuracy of the legend, but what is beyond doubt is that the distance of the most logical route to run from Marathon to Athens, going to the south of a mountain that lies in a direct path between the two, is around 40 kilometers, or 25 miles.

The organizers of the 1896 Olympic Games decided to include a foot race from Marathon to Athens as a way to honor Philippides and Greece's glorious past and to draw attention to the games. The first Olympic marathon for men was held on April 10, 1896. We do not know the exact distance, but it is said to have been around 40 kilometers. (Technically, this was not the first marathon, as the organizers held two qualifying events on the Olympic course in the weeks leading up to the games.) Seventeen runners started the race, of whom thirteen were Greek, and nine finished. The winner of the gold medal for the Olympic marathon in 1896 was a Greek man named Spyridon Louis. He finished in a time of 2 hours, 58 minutes, and 50 seconds.

So why is the marathon distance we run today fixed at an odd distance, probably longer than the 1896 event? After Athens, the summer Olympic Games continued every four years: in Paris in 1900, St. Louis in 1904, London in 1908, and Stockholm in 1912. The 1916 games awarded to Berlin were cancelled because of World War I. The games were next held in Belgium in the city of Antwerp in 1920. At each of these Olympics, a road race for men of around 40 kilometers was held, but the exact distance varied and was determined by the local organizing committee, who decided upon a route.

In 1921, after discussing the matter for several years, the International Amateur Athletic Federation (IAAF), as it was then called, decided to standardize the Olympic marathon distance and chose the length of the course that had been run in London at the 1908 games. It appears these were the first games where the course had been measured accurately. The original plan in 1908 had been to run from a starting point in the town of Windsor, outside London, to the Olympic Stadium at White City, finishing with a lap of the track, a distance of approximately 40 kilometers. The royal family, however, intervened. Windsor Castle is the official residence of the British royal family, and they asked for the course to be extended to start outside the entrance to the castle. They also asked that the race finish right in front of the royal box in the stadium, which shortened the distance to be run on the track. These tweaks meant the final distance was 42.195 kilometers, or 26 miles and 385 yards. The Olympic Marathon has been precisely this distance at every Olympics since the 1924 games in Paris.

As a side note, I find it rather interesting that races of the original marathon distance of 40 kilometers simply do not exist, or at least I have never heard of one. I have run races, many of them, over 10, 20, 30, and 50 kilometers, but not 40 kilometers. I suppose race directors know that anyone who is willing to train to run a 40k is going to want to say afterward that they ran a full marathon.

Let's talk about the Boston Marathon, the world's oldest annual marathon, held for the first time in the spring of 1897, a year after the first modern Olympic Games in Athens and inspired by its success. There were fifteen entrants that year. Until 1923, the race started in the town of Ashland and finished in Boston, a distance of a little under 40k. In 1924, in recognition of the IAAF decision to standardize the length of the Olympic Marathon, the start was moved to the town of Hopkinton, to the west of Ashland, so the race could be lengthened to the new permanent Olympic distance. The race continued every year thereafter on the same course on the third Monday in April, Patriots' Day, until 2019. Patriots' Day is a holiday in Massachusetts and in five other states commemorating the early battles of the American Revolutionary War.[30] World Wars did not stop the Boston Marathon, but the COVID-19 pandemic caused the 2020 event to be cancelled. For the first time since 1897, there was no Boston Marathon. The event returned in 2021 but was delayed until October, the first time it was not held in April.

Despite fairly tough qualifying time requirements, the size of the field has grown steadily through the history of the race and now numbers over 30,000. Runners now start in four separate waves to spread out the large field, with the faster runners going first and the slowest in the last wave. Boston is the only major marathon where the only way to get in is to meet the qualifying time by running a marathon. Until recent years, if you met the qualifying standard (currently 3 hours for a man under 40, 3 hours 30 minutes for a woman), you were guaranteed to get in. No longer is this the case, so popular has Boston become. Alas, if you decide to run only one marathon, like my professor, it will not be Boston because of the requirement to post a qualifying marathon time in order to enter.

I have run Boston four times over a twenty-year period between 1992 and 2013—the year of the bombing I write about in chapter 1—and it is one of my favorite marathons, partly because it is a point-to-point course, which I like, but more especially because there are over half a million spectators along the course to cheer you on, with ever-increasing numbers as you near the finish in downtown Boston. (I had also secured an entry for the centennial event in 1997 but was not able to participate because of other commitments; I got a friend who ran it to pick up my centennial T-shirt, which I still have.) I have, sadly, never mastered the course. I have finished many marathons feeling strong but not Boston. The first half is not difficult and one tends to go too fast, especially in the early stages of the race, which includes a lot of downhill running. The famous "Heartbreak Hill" starts at 16 miles (around 25 kilometers) and much of the following 5 miles (8 kilometers) is uphill; these hills arrive at a stage in the race when most casual runners like me are starting to tire. By the time I get to the long downhills into Boston over the last 5 miles (8 kilometers), I find I have little energy left to take advantage of the easiest part of the course. Fortunately, all the cheering from the large crowds is a big help to get to the finish line. I love Boston.

Then there is the Yonkers Marathon, the second oldest in the United States but very different. Its origin goes back to 1907. It has missed some years along the way, as the ninetieth running of Yonkers was not until 2015. I have not been able to establish why years were missed. Despite where the city of Yonkers is located, just to the north of New York City, it has for many years been a low-key event and, in recent times, has attracted a mere 100 to 200 runners. I ran it in 1988 and 1989, and the field was around that size then. I cannot think of another marathon I have run with a field that small. The appeal for me was that, by finishing it, you were assured of a place in the next New York City Marathon and thereby avoided the dreaded lottery which most runners need to enter in the hope of running New York. (My friend who picked up my Boston centennial T-shirt entered the New York Marathon lottery five times before he finally got in, as did I that same year, so we ran it together.) Frankly, I was surprised when I ran Yonkers that more runners did not take advantage of the helpful reward for running it, something that fell away years ago. As with many marathons today, other than the large city marathons, Yonkers now holds a half-marathon and a 5k at the same time to swell the numbers.

As an aside, back when I ran the Yonkers Marathon, it was held in April on a Sunday, the day before Boston. Both years, I met crazy runners at the start who were doing Boston the next day as well!

So, to run the oldest marathon in the United States, you have to be pretty good and have an entry accepted many months ahead of race day, while the second oldest is open to anyone who wants to run a marathon but without the fanfare and thousands of spectators.

In a way, Boston and Yonkers are examples of the two types of marathons on offer: the large-scale city marathon and the smaller events that often have a concurrent half-marathon and sometimes a 10k or 5k, which attract more runners and contribute to the costs of staging the event. I am going to call them "country marathons"— they do not take place on city streets; they are run in smaller towns, on suburban or country roads, or some combination.

Arguably, Boston was the first city marathon, although, unlike many on the calendar today, which take the runner on a tour of some of a city's best-known sites, Boston starts in the outer suburbs, heads toward the city, and finishes in the center of Boston on one of its best-known streets. It is one of the six that make up the World Marathon Majors series. The others are New York, Chicago, Berlin, London, and Tokyo. All are in the northern hemisphere, three in the spring and three in the fall, so elite runners can do two of them in a given year if they wish, though I should add the COVID-19 pandemic disrupted the staging and timing of these events.

City marathons, as a concept, really date back to the 1970s with many added in the years since—all over the world. Berlin goes back to 1974, and New York moved from laps around Central Park to the city streets in 1976. The Chicago Marathon began in 1977. The other World Marathon Majors, London and Tokyo, both had their debut in 1981. The number of city marathons grew rapidly in the 1980s and 1990s to the point where there might well be more cities in the world with a population over one million that hold a marathon than do not. I have not tried to check this, but it would not surprise me, so popular have city marathons become. They can provide a major boost to the local economy during the period around the event.

Linked to the growth in the number of city marathons has been the growth in the fields, to the point where the most popular city marathons, including all the majors, are difficult to get into for the average runner. I remember going to the start line in Boston for the first time in 1992, standing in the middle of the pack and crossing the start line fifteen to twenty seconds after the horn sounded. In 2013, it took me several minutes, and I was in the third and last wave at the start line. There are now four waves.

The good thing is there are now literally hundreds of city marathons all over the world from which to choose, and many of them are fairly easy to gain entry to and do not have qualifying times. Memorable city marathons I have run include Miami and San Francisco in the United States, and Rotterdam and Milan in Europe. So, if you do want to run just one marathon, why not plan a trip to a city you have always wanted to visit around the time of its city marathon? One bit of advice: plan your travel so the marathon is at the start of the visit so you can relax and celebrate for the remainder of the trip.

In terms of planning on the day of the race, I should note that many city marathons start and finish at different places; Boston, London, and New York are examples. The race organization will either arrange transport to the starting line as part of your entry fee (as Boston and New York do) or will advise runners how to get to the start using public transport. Given the large numbers at many city marathons, it is generally not practical to have someone drive you to the start; in some cases, private cars cannot get anywhere near the starting area.

While taking part in city marathons requires a good deal of planning (unless you choose one close to where you live), country marathons generally do not, and if you pick one within driving distance, it can be a day's outing. Some will even take entries on the day of the race, but not all. On the two occasions I ran the Yonkers Marathon, I drove to the start, checked in, ran the race, got in my car, and drove home. Yonkers is a circular course that starts and finishes at the same place. Most country marathons are circular or out-and-back courses (or some combination of the two), which makes the logistics of taking part easier. When a marathon starts and finishes in different places, it gets more complicated. Some will shuttle runners back to the start from the finish area—you need to check the instructions to entrants.

Let me mention one other marathon. In Connecticut, where I live, there are usually two or three marathons on the running calendar. The best known one, the Hartford Marathon, started in 1993 and is the only one in Connecticut that has been on the calendar for some years. It is typical of hundreds of marathons around the United States. It starts and finishes in the center of Hartford, a midsize city and the capital of Connecticut, but much of the course takes the runners out of town into the countryside. I have run it twice; it is about an hour from where I live, so I can drive there, run the race, and drive home, all in half a day or so. It is fairly flat and fast, and I have used it as a qualifying marathon for Boston. The event also includes a four-person marathon relay, which I have done with work colleagues, as well as a half-marathon and a 5k. These other events make this the largest running event in the state.

The website runningintheusa.com lists about 1,000 marathons in the United States, so there are many from which to choose. You read about marathoners who have done at least one in all fifty states, and a while ago, I read about a runner who accomplished this in one year—quite a feat. When I lived in Europe I found there were hundreds of marathons across the continent from which to choose. Like Hartford, the vast majority of marathons offer other distances as well, often a half-marathon, which allows a group of family members or friends from a running club who want to run different distances to all take part.

I have run some marathons where these various events start at different times or even at different locations in the same general area. In many cases, however, they start together, or within a few minutes of each other. Hartford is one of those—runners for the marathon, half-marathon, and marathon relay start out together. I always find this somewhat disconcerting, as it can cause marathon entrants to run too fast in the early stages. Those at the start line doing the marathon will be a minority. Many more will be running the half-marathon, and the relay runners at events like Hartford will be running only a quarter of the marathon distance, or around 10k. This mixed field can make it difficult to find your rhythm, as most of those running faster than you are not doing the marathon. In these situations, I find it is important to tune out what is going on around me, try to run my own pace, and look at my watch at every distance marker to check I am not going too fast in relation to my time goal.

Then, if the course brings you back to the start / finish area at the halfway mark for the half-marathoners to finish, as is often the case, it gets rather lonely in the second half of the marathon, as you have far fewer runners around, just as you start to tire. I have found the early part of the second half rather tough psychologically, until I get used to running with much less company.

On balance, I would recommend a big city marathon for your first marathon, especially if it may be your only one. I described my first marathon, in Johannesburg, South Africa, in chapter 1. Rather like Hartford, it started and finished in the city, but much of the course wound its way through open countryside, with few runners around me and no spectators. One's first marathon can be a much more memorable experience than that, and it should be.

So, let's talk about how you prepare for your first marathon. In chapter 7, where I discuss running injuries, I described what happened to me, and could happen to you, if you are too ambitious early in your running career. I would think twice about running a marathon in your first year of regular running. Yes, you might well finish, but you want the experience to be an enjoyable one for which you have fully prepared—and you do not want to get injured.

Get into running gradually, and when you are ready to start racing, focus on shorter distances from 5k to 10k as discussed in the last chapter. Build up from there over a period of months to running distances like the half-marathon. I recommend running several half-marathons, not just one, before you attempt a marathon. If you can find 30k or 20-mile races where you live, do one or more of those, it will make a big difference to your marathon preparation. As I mentioned in the last chapter, there are not many races on the calendar at these distances, which is a pity, as it is a huge leap from running a half-marathon to running a marathon.

In fact, I have long considered the psychological halfway point in a marathon, and arguably the physiological halfway point as well, to be around the 20-mile or 30k mark. When you reach this point, you have a 10k still to run, but your legs are tired, your energy stores are depleted, your mind is looking for respite, and you have to dig deep to complete that last 10k. It helps enormously, I believe, if you have raced this far before, and it is only the last 10k or so that is venturing into unknown territory. I try to think of this as a mental halfway mark in terms of effort required to run a marathon and to ignore the distance halfway marker, at which point you should still be feeling good. If not, there is trouble ahead!

I therefore suggest doing at least three training runs of around 20 miles or 30 kilometers before your first marathon; a race of this distance can be one of them (if you find such a race). You need to build up stamina for the marathon by doing these longer runs. While I do most of my running alone, I find doing a run that will take two to three hours by myself can be quite boring. It can be more enjoyable to do at least some of these longer runs with a friend, a group from a running club, or an informal network of local runners.

You can find many books and articles with training schedules for a first marathon, prepared by experts, so I am not going to present one. I will, however, offer a few further thoughts to help you to be well prepared with a good chance of enjoying the experience:

1. A training program for a first marathon should be at least six months long, built off a base of regular running, including some 5k to 10k races and half-marathons.
2. Do not feel you have to run every day; four to five days a week is fine.

3.　Gradually increase the weekly total distance as the weeks go by, as well as the distance of a weekly long run. Try to build up to around 50 miles (80 kilometers) a week, if you can, for three to four weeks leading up to the marathon, and then reduce the distance in the two weeks before the race, with very little running in the week of the race.

4.　Do not feel you need to run the marathon distance in training, but, as I said, make sure to put in the 20-mile or 30-kilometer training runs; don't do more than one per week.

5.　For a first marathon, do not worry about speed work in training; that can come later as an aid to improving marathon times, if you so desire. The most important thing preparing for a first marathon is to get used to spending a few hours on your feet running.

6.　If you pick up a minor injury, do not stress about it. In a six-month training program, missing a few days, or a week, is not going to make much difference.

Let's now talk about actually running your first marathon after months of preparation. The most important thing, surely, is to enjoy the experience. If you can, avoid the temptation to set a target time; if you cannot, be realistic, and set one you are likely to achieve. As mentioned earlier there is a rule of thumb that you can predict your marathon time by multiplying your 10k time by five. If you hope to break four hours in your first marathon, you should be running a 10k in around 48 minutes. There are no guarantees, but this gives you a guide.

I cannot stress too much the importance of starting the race slowly. Most of us go out way too fast; a marathon is a long distance, and one needs to conserve energy. If you find you have lots of energy left with 10k to go, that is the time to pick up the pace, but, let me assure you, this hardly ever happens with beginners. Just watch a big city marathon on TV as the four-to-five-hour plus runners struggle through the last 5k to 10k. Most of them would have posted faster times if they had run more conservatively in the first half of the race. I know this only too well; the occasions when I have paced myself well in a marathon are easily outnumbered by those when I have not.

On a flattish course, world-class runners will generally run negative splits, running the second half faster than the first, picking up the pace toward the end. This is hard to do when one ventures into the unknown as a beginner, but I can assure you that you will have a better experience if the two halves are close in time; the second half should be five to ten minutes slower at worst. Start out with that in mind.

Runners ask if it is OK to walk part of the way in a marathon. The reality is that most four-to-five-hour runners will find they have no choice in the latter stages, and most runners do not walk until their body tells them they have to walk. My advice to anyone expecting to run four hours plus is to stop at all the refreshment stations, take a drink, and then walk a bit to catch your breath before starting to run again. This may seem ridiculous when you get to the first station, but it will pay dividends handsomely later in the race. From the start of a marathon, try to discipline yourself to walk, for a minute at most, and then start running again. It will get more difficult to get going again as the race progresses, but this should be the goal.

You might have heard about runners "hitting the wall" somewhere in the second half of a marathon. Let me provide a very basic and nonscientific explanation of what this means. The energy we use when we run comes from two sources: glycogen (carbohydrates), which is stored in the muscles and the liver, and triglycerides (body fats). Glycogen is a form of glucose and is the high octane fuel that provides the primary source of energy when we exercise. The amount that the body can store is limited and will become completely depleted during the course of an event as long as a marathon. Once this happens, the athlete is totally dependent on low octane fuel in the form of body fats as an energy source. The point at which glycogen stores are exhausted is the so-called wall—the physical effort required to run increases noticeably.

One can replace the glycogen stored in the liver to some extent during the race by drinking sports drinks at the refreshment stations, consuming fructose-based energy gels, or—a favorite of mine whenever I can lay my hands on one—eating half of a banana. I should add that it is a good idea to try different energy gels in training to find one you like. The body cannot, however, replace glycogen stores at anywhere near the rate at which one consumes them, so ingesting sugar in any form during the marathon will only delay the exhaustion of glycogen stores but will not prevent it from happening.

In a marathon, it is critical to consume carbohydrates in some form to avoid the risk of hypoglycemia (low blood sugar). The brain and central nervous system require a continual supply of glucose via the bloodstream to function. Early symptoms of low blood sugar can include light-headedness, dizziness, and impaired judgment. Regular consumption of energy gels during the marathon is a good way to prevent this. If it occurs while running a marathon, however, it is a sign that one urgently needs to ingest a significant amount of sugar in some form, such as a sports drink.

Let me give you a personal example from my two Yonkers Marathons, back in 1988 and 1989. In the first one, I assumed the refreshment stations would have energy drinks as well as water, but they did not. They only had water, and I had not brought any energy gels to carry with me. Energy gels were something of a novelty back then. Around the 20-mile (32-kilometer) mark, I became lightheaded and was forced to slow down in order to finish the race. I recognized the signs of hypoglycemia. I crossed the finish line, received my medal, and walked to my car to change into warm clothes. I knew I was not capable of driving safely, and I was alone. Fortunately, I had brought along two bananas to eat afterward; I ate them and sat in the car for around twenty minutes until my blood sugar level felt normal, and I was able to drive. At the time, I was fit, running around 100 kilometers, or 60 miles, a week, and was well prepared to run a marathon; if I had not been, I doubt I would have finished the race.

The following year, I brought along energy gels to consume with water during the race, and a friend who lived in the area provided me with energy drinks at a number of points along the course. The difference was amazing compared to the previous year. I had done much less training in the three months leading up to the race—averaging around 30 kilometers or 20 miles a week—and was two minutes slower at halfway, but I never had to slow down as the race progressed and finished feeling strong. My time for the second half was 17 minutes faster than it was the year before. I had run the same course on far less training; the difference was replacing carbohydrates at regular intervals during the race.

A few years before that, I had run an ultramarathon and was taking a new energy replacement drink at the refreshment stations. I had tried it in training and found that I liked the taste. It turned out it did not contain a sufficient quantity of carbohydrates, and I became seriously hypoglycemic with about a quarter of the race to go. They also had Coca-Cola at the refreshment stations; I stopped at the next one and consumed as much as I could manage, knowing its sugar content is high, and recovered completely within the next ten minutes or so.

As I said, body fat is a low octane fuel, but even a slender human body contains enough of it to allow a well-trained athlete to keep running for a long time. A novice runner will derive some of the required energy from body fat right from the start of a marathon; however, the blend of glycogen to body fat consumed will be tilted more toward glycogen than would be the case in a seasoned, fit athlete. This means the beginner will consume all the glycogen stores earlier in the race than an experienced runner. To change the blend to more body fat requires extensive training and running long distances. Without getting into the physiological details, over time, the body adapts to burning more body fat and less glycogen. This is why the long training runs are so important before attempting to run a marathon. The body gradually learns, through repeatedly running for over two hours, that the glycogen stores will become depleted and adapts to make them last longer. If you continue to run marathons and train for them adequately, you will find this process continues, and your times should improve for several years regardless of the age at which you start. A former training partner broke three hours in a marathon for the first time shortly before his sixtieth birthday, having only started to run five years earlier. My fastest marathon was six years after my first, at the age of thirty-three. My times improved rapidly over the first year or so and then in smaller increments over the next five.

Finally, I would like to touch on the question of diet—but just for the week or so leading up to a marathon. The question of diet for every life is beyond the scope of this book. Until the 1990s, there was a widely held belief that carbo-loading would be of benefit for running a marathon. In the days leading up to the event, the runner would eat a diet rich in carbohydrates and lower than one's normal diet in fats and protein. A plate of pasta with a sauce is a good example. The conventional wisdom was that this would enable the runner to go to the start with stores of glycogen at their maximum. I did this many times in preparing to run a marathon in the 1970s and 1980s, but not always. I was, however, never wholly convinced that carbo-loading gave me an edge.

Experts started to question this approach in the 1990s. Some have advocated a diet low in carbohydrates and high in fats instead, to train the body to burn fats efficiently. While an approach like this might be appropriate for an experienced and highly trained marathon runner, my own, unscientific view is that a beginner needs to have a full supply of glycogen at the start of the race. Carbo-loading in the days leading up to the race is not an approach I would use today. My advice, based on my personal experience running many marathons, is to stick to a diet of roughly 50 percent carbohydrate, 30 percent fat, and 20 percent protein. There is plenty of advice from experts one can find to support this approach.

Finally, if the marathon is in the morning, as most are, I recommend you do not go to the start on an empty stomach, as your glycogen stores in the liver will not be at their maximum after a night's sleep. It is important to ingest some carbohydrates a couple of hours before the start, in the form of a sports drink, energy gel, or food that is easily digestible, such as a banana. I have done this since the early days of my running career for races of any distance.

In conclusion, I have tried to share some basic advice on preparing for and running a first marathon, the classic long-distance road race. If you follow this approach, I am confident your first marathon experience will be one you will cherish for the rest of your life. You may even be tempted to run a second one. And a few runners will be tempted to go longer than the marathon and enter the world of ultramarathons. More on that in the next chapter.

CHAPTER 11

Beyond the Marathon

I remember vividly the first ultramarathon I entered—the Matopos 33 Miler, as it was called at the time, in Bulawayo, Zimbabwe, on Easter Saturday, 1975. First run in 1963, the race starts at 6:00 a.m., as it is getting light, in the Matobo National Park, a UNESCO World Heritage Site, south of the city. The Matobo Hills have stunning scenery and abundant wildlife, including leopards and rhinos. Back when I ran it, the race had a field of around 200 runners and was started with two bugle players breaking the dawn silence. The first 10k of the route is on a circular road in the park itself, closed to traffic at this early hour, passing a well-known viewpoint known as "World's View." There is not a sound beyond the birds chirping and the occasional chatter of the runners, an awesome experience. After leaving the park, one heads north on the road toward Bulawayo. There are several hills along the way; in fact, one crosses from the watershed of the Limpopo River (Zimbabwe's southern border) into the watershed of the Zambezi River (Zimbabwe's northern border).

With the small field in 1975, the runners became rather spread out in the latter stages of the race, and I found myself running alone for much of the last hour, but the camaraderie I had felt among the runners in the early part of the race continued to provide motivation. As I ran more ultramarathons, I learned this is typical of races beyond the marathon with their smaller fields. Ultramarathon runners chat with strangers at the start line and run with fellow competitors they just met to have company along the way, striking up conversations and getting to know one another—something that is not typical with larger fields in marathons.

Nevertheless, I was happy to finally enter the sports club where the Matopos finished and complete a lap of the field with people cheering me on, even though I was a good hour and a half behind the winner. I doubt they do this today, but when I ran this race, every finisher was called up at the prize-giving to collect a small shield for completing the race as well as a certificate stating one's finishing position and time. I still have the shield on my shelf to this day. These days, the Matopos Ultra-Marathon, as it is now known, is part of a large-scale running event that includes an ultramarathon relay, a half-marathon, a 10k, and a 5k fun run. Like races everywhere, the event has been interrupted by the pandemic but will rebound, of that I am sure.

This was my memorable introduction to road races longer than the marathon. In the next chapter, I describe the famous Comrades Marathon, a race of around 56 miles (or 90 kilometers), which I have run a number of times; however, this chapter is devoted to distances I rather like and have raced over thirty times, 30 to 35 miles, or say 50 to 60 kilometers. On the US racing calendar, you will also find 50-mile races, 100-kilometer races, and 100-mile races—on roads as well as on trails for all these distances. Plus, there is the famous Badwater 135-mile ultramarathon, staged in the hottest part of California in midsummer, as well as a few races longer than that, for those who are up for it. This is not my thing and never has been. There are books devoted to racing these very long distances; this is simply not one of them.

Yet some people become addicted to these very long distances and it is encouraging to read about someone who has replaced an addiction to narcotics with an addiction to long distance running. An article on the BBC website includes the following piece written by a female runner from California:[31]

At 27, I was arrested and spent the night in a prison cell. That was the worst experience of my life and scared me into getting clean... I was put on a six-month rehab program where I had to go to a Narcotics Anonymous meeting every day. After six months, I was clean. Now I've been clean for 25 years. I started running because I was searching for something to take the place of drugs. I ran a 10k (six miles) on a whim after seeing a flyer for it and, three months later, I ran my first marathon. Ultras followed soon after. I've run 100, 200 and 300-mile races. When you finally stop running after that long, it feels great. You've accomplished something huge and it's like, "Wow!" I definitely get a kind of high. I'm one of about only a dozen people in the world who has run 100 miles (161km) more than 100 times. You could definitely say that I'm addicted.

I shall just say that races of around 50k are certainly worth considering for anyone who has done the marathon distance and enjoyed it and is looking for something different. Firstly, the setting for races of 50k or longer is generally in contrast with a typical marathon. As I discussed in chapter 10, to many runners, marathons mean "city marathons" with huge fields and thousands of spectators cheering you on as you run through city streets. I am not aware of any large-scale city 50k races. Races of 50k and upward are generally not held in cities, though there are some exceptions. I once ran a 50k in New York that consisted of laps in Central Park; while the location was in the middle of Manhattan, it was not on the roads. What this race had in common with most 50k events was a relatively small field and few spectators.

If you look at the calendar for ultras on the website runningintheusa.com (probably the most comprehensive list of races in the United States), you will find:

- There are many of them every month of the year and all over the United States.
- Many offer several distances, such as 25k, marathon distance, 50k, and 50 miles.
- More of these events are on trails than on roads.

Offering several distances gives runners options and, for the organizers, is going to attract a larger field. Someone who would give a 50k race a miss might be up for a 25k race. You can find races on this site that offer as many as six distances from which to choose.

In the United States, these longer distances of 50k and up are aimed more at devotees of trail running than those who race on roads. Many of them are in mountainous terrain and quite demanding. Times tend to be slower than on the roads. As I mentioned earlier, I love being in nature and running on trails away from traffic but have seldom raced more than 10k on trails. Longer trail races are a sport in themselves but not one I ever got into having always lived in or around cities. There are so many in the United States that one could participate in one practically every week of the year if prepared to travel. There are books out there devoted solely to long-distance trail running if you are interested.

Many of the races of the 50k to 60k distance I have done earlier in my career were on the roads in South Africa, where road ultramarathons are very popular. I enjoyed running ultramarathons as a challenge. Usually there is a marker to indicate the marathon distance; it can be daunting seeing it for the first time and realizing you still have a way to go. One inevitably runs an ultramarathon at a slower pace than a marathon, and times do not have the same significance. As a result, there is not the same pressure against the clock as there is in a marathon, which is nice. What tends to impress people is the distance run rather than the time. As a running mate once told me, "What I like about ultras is that I am not expected to run fast." Runners often ask me my best marathon time, but I do not remember ever being asked my best time for a 50k, not even when wearing a T-shirt from a 50k race and having people observe how impressive it is to run that far.

Running 50k or beyond requires a great deal of training. Without adequate preparation, including a number of long training runs, the last part of a 50k after the marathon distance can be very tough going, as glycogen stores are totally depleted, and the legs are tired.

However, a benefit I have found from running ultramarathons is that they help build stamina for improving one's performance in races of shorter distances. Running a 50k race will not improve your outright speed—one needs to do speed work for that—but it will help you to run at close to your current optimal racing pace for longer. I explained what I mean by speed work in chapter 6.

In particular, training and racing beyond the marathon mark should help improve marathon times; you will feel the fatigue that sets in during the last quarter of a marathon less as your body adapts to running long distances. I recorded my fastest marathon time some five weeks after running the 90k Comrades ultramarathon, sufficient time to recover but now with my stamina at a higher level. My experience is that ultramarathons should help you run better times over any distance up to and including the marathon.

There is an early spring 50k road race called the Sybil Ludington 50k Run a half an hour from where I live. It is a hilly and scenic circular course in a quiet part of New York state, around an hour from the city. I ran it fairly hard the year I turned sixty with insufficient training for this distance, which meant I was totally exhausted at the end of it. Race officials gave me the good news that I had set a new age-group record. Once I had recovered from the race, however, I found my fitness had moved up a level; I was enjoying my training runs more and running faster times in races over the shorter distances during the late spring and into summer.

I did not go back to this event for another ten years but decided to enter it again when I found out that the seventy age-group record was one I should be able to beat. In fact, I learned that my sixty age-group still stood. I had done more long runs this time but was ten years older. I paced myself well and felt quite good at the end. Though I was around forty-five minutes slower this time, I crushed the age-group record. Again, after a couple of weeks of recovery, I was running races over the shorter distances faster than I had for some time and winning my age division regularly.

I shall mention one other ultramarathon on the roads that I think is worth traveling a long way to run, and that is the Two Oceans Marathon in the beautiful city of Cape Town in South Africa.[32] Entry is through a lottery system and the field is limited to around 14,000, however, a number of places are set aside every year for international entrants. I ran it three times much earlier in my career and had one very good run by my standards, under four hours. It follows a circular course, starting and finishing in the city's southern suburbs. It is 56 kilometers, around 35 miles. Until the half-marathon mark, it is flat, and one can easily find oneself going faster than one should, because there are big climbs to come. The course skirts along the west side of False Bay, passing through picturesque villages, to a town called Fish Hoek, where one makes a right turn, to the east, away from the Indian Ocean to head toward the Atlantic Ocean. What follows is a long climb up a pass called Chapman's Peak, carved into the side of a mountain, and then all the way back down to sea level at Hout Bay. False Bay is Indian Ocean water, and Hout Bay is much colder Atlantic Ocean water, hence the name of the race. Dip your toe in at both bays, and you will instantly know which has water carried from Antarctica by an ocean current.

In the village of Hout Bay, one turns to the north. As one passes the marathon marker coming out of the village, one is starting the longest climb of the race, up to Constantia Nek. This is where many runners are reduced to a walk. From Constantia Nek, a long, winding, scenic downhill section follows and then a flat stretch to the finish line. A magnificent race it is, very popular and well worth the journey if one wants a memorable experience running an ultramarathon, even just once.

The author, in the middle of the photo in the light top with a diagonal
stripe, running the1976 Comrades Marathon.

CHAPTER 12

The Ultimate Human Race

On Sunday, June 13, 2021, more than a year after the start of the COVID-19 pandemic, I ran a virtual race. There were 14,491 runners participating over five distances offered, from 5k up to 90k. I was one of 3,499 who ran the 10k distance that was offered, and I finished third out of forty-nine in my division.

Why would nearly 15,000 runners take part in a one-day virtual race, 865 of whom ran 90k?

The answer is that 2021 was the one-hundredth anniversary of the first Comrades Marathon, a hugely popular ultramarathon in South Africa, more than twice the distance of a standard marathon and nicknamed "The Ultimate Human Race." Due to the pandemic, there was no Comrades Marathon in 2020 or 2021 so the race organizers, the Comrades Marathon Association, offered a virtual race called "Comrades Hope Challenge" instead, on the day in June when the race is normally held. One of the goals was to raise money for charities involved in addressing the social consequences of the pandemic. The actual race is around 90k (about 56 miles)—hence the opportunity to run a 90k virtual race. You could run wherever in the world you were located on the day—I was at home in Connecticut and ran a favorite 10k training route—though I imagine that quite a number of those who ran 90k, did so on the actual grueling course of the Comrades. Fortunately, the real Comrades Marathon returned in August 2022, with a slightly reduced field compared to recent years due to the continuing presence of COVID-19.

The Comrades Marathon was started in 1921 by a South African veteran of the First World War in memory of his fallen comrades.

It was run from the city of Pietermaritzburg, capital of the province of KwaZulu-Natal, to Durban, the province's largest city and a major port on the Indian Ocean coast. As I mentioned, the distance of the race was, and still is, around 90k or 56 miles. Thirty-four runners started that first race, and seventeen finishers are listed in the official results.[33] The winning time of 8 hours and 59 minutes was the slowest in the history of the race; it seems no one was in a hurry to get to Durban. The following year they decided to run the race in the other direction, starting in Durban at sea level and running inland, finishing in Pietermaritzburg at an altitude of around 2,000 feet. The number of finishers increased to twenty-six and started a tradition that continues to this day, of an "up run" and a "down run" in alternating years. Times on the up run are somewhat slower for the average runner, but only marginally so for elite athletes.

The race took place as an annual event for twenty years until 1940 and then was not held for five years during World War II, resuming in 1946. The number of participants remained small for the first forty years; the first year with over one hundred finishers—all men in those days—was 1962. After that, the size of the field grew steadily, especially from the 1970s onward, when the running revolution got underway.

I first ran the Comrades in 1975. As it was the fiftieth running of the race, the organizers broke with tradition and decided on an "up run," the same direction as the race had been in 1974, so the race could finish in Pietermaritzburg on the grounds of the Collegian Harriers Club, which organized the race at the time. Today this large-scale event is managed by the Comrades Marathon Association, based at Comrades House in the city. The building includes a small museum showcasing the history of the race.

The number of finishers reached 1,000 for the first time in 1973, and there were over 1,000 finishers in 1974 as well. In planning the 1975 race, the organizers had a feeling many former Comrades runners, who had not done the race for years, would return for the golden jubilee race. In those days, there were no refreshment stations along the route, so every runner needed a crew in a car to drive along the route and provide drinks, and the road became quite congested. The organizers decided the maximum number of runners the route could reasonably accommodate was 1,500. Entries would be accepted from previous Comrades finishers up to this number. Entries would only be accepted from novices like me if there were spots left over to reach the 1,500 maximum. Novices had to submit a qualifying standard marathon time with their provisional entry, and any remaining spots would be awarded in order of times. I picked a fast course for my qualifier, a marathon that also finishes in Pietermaritzburg, and submitted a time of 3 hours and 27 minutes. In the end, entries were accepted from around 150 novices, and the cut came at 3 hours and 32 minutes, a mere five minutes slower than my time. I was in the field for the golden jubilee Comrades. Sadly, a work colleague with whom I had trained missed the cut by a few minutes. In the end, 1,352 started the race. As with many large races, entries close weeks before the event and inevitably some entrants pick up injuries or illnesses or cannot make it to the start line for other reasons.

The Comrades route is tough and includes five major climbs and several shorter ones that are also serious hills. Flat sections of any length are few. The highest point is at 2,850 feet. While the route, all on a two-lane road in those days, was congested especially in the first half of the race, seeing my friends at regular intervals as they drove along the route to provide me with drinks and encouragement was a luxury that is rare today—only possible, if it is allowed, in races with very small fields.

The 1975 Comrades was the first race I had run with anything more than a handful of spectators watching. There was a large crowd at the start outside the Durban City Hall, spectators all along the main street in Pinetown, a town about a quarter of the way into the race, and from the point where one enters Pietermaritzburg, all the way to the finish. In fact, small groups of spectators were scattered along the entire 90k course. Today the crowds watching the Comrades Marathon are much larger than in 1975; nevertheless, it was an uplifting experience for me to be cheered on by spectators, especially in the latter stages of the race when fatigue has set in; their support made a huge difference.

It is hard to describe the exhilaration I felt as I finally entered the Collegian Harriers grounds to run a lap around a grass field to the finish line in front of the cheering crowd, including my own crew of three. In fact, I passed three runners on the field to finish 652 out of the 1,237 who finished within the allowed time of 11 hours. My time was 8 hours and 54 minutes. Although I ran the Comrades on twelve more occasions over a twenty-five-year period, recording times more than two hours faster than 1975, no feeling, no sense of accomplishment, in another Comrades or any other race I have done can compare with how I felt that day. A special medal was awarded that year to mark the fiftieth Comrades, which I cherish to this day. If you are into ultramarathons or want to try just one, consider traveling to the Comrades Marathon. The qualification times to enter are not too demanding. No other race of this kind of distance anywhere else in the world attracts a field of over 20,000 runners, nor the tens of thousands of spectators along the route from start to finish.

South Africa was undergoing social change in the 1970s, as cracks began to appear in apartheid, and 1975 was the first year the field was not restricted to white athletes. I was honored to be a part of the first multiracial Comrades. A relatively small number of Black athletes took part, with a best placing of nineteenth. Today athletes of color tend to dominate the race. Women were still not allowed to compete in 1975, though I saw one or two on the course, determined to take part even if unofficially. In the years since, the Comrades Marathon Association has combed through the results, and where they have been able to identify females who took part, perhaps using a man's race number, they have amended the results retrospectively. Women were finally allowed to enter the following year, and the official results of the 1976 race include five female finishers. It took fifty-six years from the first Comrades Marathon before the race was completely open. In both 2018 and 2019, before the pandemic, there were over 3,000 women finishers.

The size of the overall field grew steadily in the 1980s and 1990s and started to attract larger numbers of international runners, several of whom have won the race. In 1983, there were more than 5,000 finishers for the first time, and five years later, there were over 10,000. The last two Comrades before the pandemic had over 16,000 finishers, an incredible feat in organization for a race of this length, and one that has no parallel in the ultramarathon world.

The Comrades has a number of rather unique traditions, one being the different types of medals awarded. When I received my first medal in 1975, the first ten finishers received a gold medal (in earlier years, it had been only the first six), every finisher under 7 hours and 30 minutes received a silver medal, and every other finisher under 11 hours, which included me that year, received a bronze medal.

I do not know the history of the time limit for a silver medal; one needs to average roughly 8 minutes a mile, or 5 minutes a kilometer, to earn it. That is a speed to which every runner who participates in local races on the weekend can relate—I have even heard it said this is the speed that is the divide between jogging and running. It is a speed that will get you to the finish line of a marathon in three and a half hours—an average speed that is no mean feat on a course more than twice as long as a marathon with monstrous hills to climb, on both the up and down runs.

Interestingly, the cutoff times for a silver medal and a bronze medal never change regardless of the length of the course, which varies from year to year depending on the route and where the race finishes. (It always starts at the same locations in Pietermaritzburg and Durban, outside the city hall, but the finish locations have moved

over the years to accommodate larger fields.) The route, while largely similar from year to year, depends on annual discussions with the
authorities of the towns through which the race passes. The longest
race I ran was 91.4k, a year when there was a detour because of road
work along the main street of Pinetown, and the shortest was 87.6k.
These days, due to the size of the field, the race leaves or enters
Durban on a freeway, which has not only straightened out a section of the course and shortened it slightly but has also eliminated a
downhill section followed by a steep climb that was previously part
of the route.

In later years, the Comrades Marathon Association recognized
the significance to many participants of finishing in under 9 hours,
roughly 4-hour marathon pace, and introduced an additional medal,
part silver and part bronze in appearance, for those finishing in times
between 7.5 hours and 9 hours. Well under half the field typically
finishes in under 9 hours. In recent times, several other categories of
medals have been added and today there are nine categories.

After shaving more than an hour off my first Comrades time the
following year on the down run, I then collected nine successive silver medals over an eleven-year span, until I moved from South Africa
to the United States after the 1988 race. I returned to South Africa
to run the seventieth Comrades in 1995 and the seventy-fifth Comrades in 2000 and added two of these part-silver medals, specially
designed for the respective anniversaries, to my collection, finishing
in a little under 8 hours on both occasions.

The 2000 up run was special; it was the millennium year, the seventy-
fifth Comrades Marathon, and for me, twenty-five years since I first
ran. For the occasion, much like in 1975, runners who had not entered
for years decided to come out and do one more Comrades. A record
23,961 runners entered the 2000 race, and there were over 20,000 finishers for the first time. One of the reasons for the large number of
entries, I believe, is that the Comrades Marathon Association decided
to allow runners an extra hour to finish the race—12 hours instead

of 11—which gave many slower runners added confidence they could earn a medal.

The extra hour was popular with the ultramarathon community, and from 2003 onward, the time allowed to finish the course was extended permanently to 12 hours. So as not to dilute the value of the bronze medal for finishing under 11 hours, those who finish between 11 and 12 hours receive a copper medal.

Besides its complex and ever-evolving medal system, Comrades is known for its race numbering system. When you enter, you receive a number to wear on the day, much like other races. If you enter the next year, you will receive the same number. This continues year after year if you continue to enter. If you do not enter, the Comrades Marathon Association will hold your number for you for two years and then allocate it to someone else if you do not return. The number I received back in 1975 when I first ran was 1203. That number had been used once by an entrant in 1969 and once by another entrant in 1972, who had not returned by 1975, so it was recycled. Over a twelve-year period, I proceeded to run ten Comrades, missing only two, so number 1203 stayed with me.

Comrades has another tradition: awarding numbers to runners in perpetuity. When this happens, the number becomes yours forever, not just for life. These are called green numbers, as they are printed on a green rather than white background. Runners who are seen in a green number at Comrades enjoy a measure of respect that is unique in the running world in my experience. There are three ways to earn a green number: three wins, five gold medals, or ten finishes. Naturally, most of us can only ever hope to achieve this by completing the race ten times. When you run your tenth and are going for your green number, you run in a yellow number, as I did in 1986; countless competitors wish you luck along the way when you are running in yellow, an awesome experience.

A ceremony is held at the finish to award embroidered cloth green numbers, suitable for framing, to those who have earned them that year. Mine was memorable as I was handed my green number 1203 by Wally Hayward, one of the Comrades Marathon all-time greats, who had won the race five times in five attempts between 1930, when he was twenty-one years old, and 1954, in addition to winning many other events around the world. When I met him, he was in his late seventies, and I remember chatting with him about his plans to enter Comrades in 1988, the year he would turn eighty, not having taken part since his last win in 1954.

His time in 1988 was a remarkable 9 hours 44 minutes, placing him around the middle of the field. I had finished the race myself earlier in the afternoon and was a spectator when he entered the stadium to a roar. Watching him circle the field, running comfortably, gave me goose bumps. He entered the down run the following year, just before his eighty-first birthday, but barely made the 11-hour cutoff for a medal. He did not run Comrades again; nevertheless, he has the distinction of being the oldest finisher of the race.[34]

I remember so well having the opportunity to meet him and enjoy a brief conversation; he exemplifies what this book is about. He died in 2006, in his ninety-eighth year, having *run for his life*, at least for most of it. His Comrades Marathon career spanned almost sixty years, quite remarkably.[35]

After completing ten and receiving my green number, I thought about calling it a day because of the time commitment to train for such a long race. But I was immediately told that Comrades tradition required running in a green number, so at least eleven it needed to be. After taking the next year off, I returned and ran in green number 1203 in 1988, a number no one else will ever wear at the Comrades Marathon. Effectively, it has been retired.

The Comrades distance marking system is also unique; the course is marked in kilometers to go. So, if the course in a given year is 89.6 kilometers long, the first marker you might see after 600 meters (but probably won't because it is dark and there are thousands of runners around you) will say "89k to go." And so it goes until you finally see "1k to go" outside the stadium.

Finally, there is a tradition surrounding the end of the race, which always finishes in a stadium with a lap of a sports field. As the race takes place in the middle of winter, when temperatures are mild but days are short, the later finishers will get to the finish line in the dark, having also started in the dark. With a minute or so to go before the cutoff time, a race official walks to the finish line with a starter's pistol; the official has his or her back to the oncoming runners, holds the pistol aloft, and looks at the official race clock. These days, this takes place with loudspeakers blasting the Swedish rock band Europe's 1980's hit "The Final Countdown." As the race clock strikes the cutoff time, now twelve hours, the official fires a blank shot into the sky to end the race, oblivious of oncoming runners who may be, and often are, no more than a second or two from finishing and earning a medal. The official cannot hear the footsteps of approaching runners; the crowd noise as the end approaches is deafening as spectators urge runners to pick up the pace and earn their medal. Inevitably, there are runners who have trained for months and run for twelve hours who miss out by the narrowest of margins. The drama that unfolds watching the last minutes of a Comrades Marathon stays with you long afterward.

At a local 16k race in early September 2022, an experienced female runner from the area where I live in Connecticut appeared at the start in a Comrades top and a Comrades cap a mere six days after completing the ninety-fifth Comrades Marathon in under twelve hours and earning a medal. (Six days is not a misprint!) She told a group of us about her memorable first Comrades experience, including how a male runner in her party who traveled from the United States to South Africa had taken seven minutes from the start of the race at precisely 5:30 a.m. to reach the start line, as he was lined up near the back of the 15,000 runners, only to miss out on a medal by less than seven minutes.

The drama of the occasion can, however, inspire those who fail. I mentioned in chapter 11 that I had run a low-key 50k road race the year I turned seventy. At the start line, I noticed a male runner, clearly in his seventies, in shorts with the colors of the South African flag. Thinking he must be a South African, I went up and introduced myself. He was, in fact, not South African; he was from New York City and was in training for the Comrades Marathon, which, at the time, was about two months away. We ran together for the first half hour, chatting away about our running careers and the races we had done.

I learned he had been traveling all the way to South Africa for several years to run the Comrades and had failed to make the twelve-hour cutoff to earn a medal, but there he was running a 50k race as part of his training to try once more. Unless you have been part of the experience, it would be hard to understand his motivation. I imagine most people he knew thought he was crazy; I could understand. For me, and for him, the Comrades Marathon is the ultimate human race.

Five veteran runners about to run a cross country race in August 2022. On the left is Roger Robinson, celebrated academic, author and octogenarian champion runner and next to him is Katherine Switzer, the first woman to run the Boston Marathon wearing an official number, back in 1967. The author is on the right alongside two fellow septuagenarians from the local running community.

CHAPTER 13

Aging and Athletic Performance

I n chapter 3, we reviewed a number of scientific studies on the benefits of running regularly. These studies provide strong evidence of reduced risk of developing common conditions associated with aging, such as cardiovascular disease and some forms of cancer, leading to a longer health span. Some of these studies conclude that one's statistical odds of living longer, in addition to living without debilitating disease, also improve with regular exercise. This is all good news.

There are several books that discuss the extraordinary age to which many people in so-called blue zones live, describing their lifestyles and the diets they follow.[36] Blue zones are areas of the world where people, according to research, seem to live longer than average. You can also read books and articles about dietary supplements that may slow the aging process. This book focuses solely on the impact of exercise on aging.

The unavoidable reality, however, is that as we age, we all slow down in a multitude of different ways, including, for runners, the times in which we run a lap on the track, around the block, or a road race over a given distance. All regular exercise can do is slow down the slowing down, which, in itself, is surely welcome news. In this chapter we'll take a look at how and why runners slow down as the years pass, referring to a study in the UK, supported by information about what has happened to me and my race times as I have aged from my thirties to my seventies.

I recently ran a low-key 10-mile (16k) race in a little over 90 minutes. It was good enough to finish first in the 70+ age-group. At my peak, in my thirties, I was able to finish a race of this distance in just over an hour—my best is 61 minutes. It is worth noting that times like that did not win me any awards earlier in life. One needs to be way under that to be competitive. The point is it is now taking me 50 percent longer to run this distance than it did in my thirties.

I now run half-marathons in around two hours, whereas my best is 81 minutes—again, a deterioration of about 50 percent over the past four decades. My times will inevitably get slower as I continue to age. In a later table, I present a snapshot of how my race times have changed over various distances through the decades, but I will refer first to a paper by Norman Lazarus and Stephen Harridge published in 2016: "Declining Performance of Master Athletes: Silhouettes of the Trajectory of Healthy Human Ageing?"[37] In this paper, they analyze world records for both men and women over two distances, 100 meters and 10,000 meters, through adulthood into old age. The first is an all-out sprint, where neuromuscular fitness is key; the latter is an endurance test—the longest standard track event and one where cardiorespiratory capacity is key. They set out the progression of world records with age in their paper, and one can observe the following:

1. The rate of decline is remarkably similar over both these distances and is similar for men and women—a roughly linear decline until around the age of seventy to seventy-five; thereafter the decline accelerates rapidly.
2. The rate of decline appears to accelerate very slightly for men around the age of fifty and then remains linear thereafter until age seventy to seventy-five. This seems to be the case for both distances. With women, the rate of decline appears almost linear until age seventy.
3. From age eighty onward, the decline is very steep for both men and women for both distances.

These observations are based on the age-group world records for the two distances at the time of their study. It is not a cross-sectional study of individual athletes who continued to compete through their adult life, which would show how the times of individuals change with aging. I have not found such a study.

I have kept a running logbook since I started running regularly and have recorded all my race times since 1974. Here are my best times on the road, for various distances, for each decade since I turned thirty:

Age Group	10km	10 Mile	Half-Marathon	Marathon	50km
30–39	37m	1h 1m	1h 21m	2h 44m	3h 24m
40–49	37m	1h 3m	1h 23m	2h 51m	3h 37m
50–59	39m	1h 4m	1h 27m	3h 8m	4h 15m
60–69	41m	1h 13m	1h 38m	3h 38m	4h 23m
At 70	47m	1h 21m	1h 49m	-	5h 16m

Some of the fluctuations are no doubt due to the difficulty of the course, as most of the times for a given distance were recorded on different courses—on three continents in fact. Also, after the age of forty, I tended to put in less training from year to year and, from the age of seventy, much less.

I would note, however, my best 10k, half-marathon, and 50k times at age sixty and a decade later at seventy were recorded in the same events near my home ten years apart, so these times are comparable. The 10k course is fairly flat and fast; the half-marathon course is hilly and not ideal for fast times. The same is true of the 50k course. These three races are held only a few weeks apart in April and May.

When I turned sixty and when I turned seventy, I ran these races as hard as I could; I had trained and was in reasonable physical shape. In fact, my times in both the 10k and 50k events broke the sixty- and seventy-age-group course records. The sixty-plus course record for the 10k stood for nine years. I believe the other three records still stand as of this writing. I should note these are times recorded in low-key events with relatively small fields and are far from world class; setting records in these races is simply an indicator that I was sufficiently fit to record reasonably respectable times.

The times seem to me to confirm the findings Lazarus and Harridge discussed in their paper. Take a look at my 10k times. I was never as competitive over this distance as I was over longer distances, with a best time of 37 minutes. From my early thirties to my early sixties, however, my best times changed by only four minutes. From sixty to seventy, however, my best time deteriorated by some six minutes and continues to slow. None of the ten-mile times are on the same course so, while indicative of a trend, are not as comparable. Over the half-marathon distance, my times changed by only a few minutes from my thirties to my fifties, but once I hit sixty, the best I could manage was 1 hour, 38 minutes, and an all-out effort ten years later on the same hilly course took 1 hour, 49 minutes. Both these times were good enough to win the age division.

The last time I had a real go at trying to break three hours for the marathon was at the Paris Marathon in 2000 when I was fifty-three. I was reasonably well trained, though not at peak fitness, and having run many marathons, I knew within half an hour or so I did not have the pace for a sub-three-hour marathon. I had a comfortable run and finished in 3 hours and 8 minutes. Can a fifty-year-old or a sixty-year-old run a marathon in under three hours? No doubt about it, but it was not to be for me on that day. My last sub-three marathon was at the New York Marathon in 1991 at the age of forty-four. The following year I moved to Europe and did not have the time, with career and family commitments, to put in the extensive training to run good marathon times for the following seven years, until Paris in 2000. In my early sixties, I recorded a best time of 3 hours, 38 minutes, at a marathon in Europe on a flat course. Two years later, I ran a qualifying marathon in 3 hours, 48 minutes, for the 2013 Boston Marathon discussed in chapter 1. I have not run the standard marathon distance since 2013 but did run the 50k referred to earlier in 2017, the year I turned seventy, and enjoyed it.

I loved road races of 50k to 56k when I was younger. I ran a lot of them in my thirties when I was living in South Africa, where there are many on offer, and I was quite good over this distance. A best time of 3 hours, 24 minutes, over 50k is running at 2-hour-52-minute marathon pace for a marathon, plus an additional 5 miles (8 kilometers) or so. The time of 4 hours, 15 minutes, recorded in my fifties, reflects a much steeper drop-off than the other distances. I don't think this means much, as I only ran one 50k race in my fifties. That was a multiple-lap course in Central Park in New York in cold and damp January weather, done as a long training run rather than as a race. As I noted earlier, however, the 50k times recorded in the year I turned sixty and in the year I turned seventy were on the same hilly course. On both occasions, I was in good condition, although lacking long training runs, and set age-group course records; these two times are comparable. I was as much as a minute per kilometer slower at the age of seventy, confirming the decline noted in the Lazarus and Harridge study.

Lazarus and Harridge speculate as to the reasons for the decline: is it due to a drop in the number of competitors as athletes age, a reduction in the intensity and time put into training as athletes age, or "fading integrative physiological capacity" despite athletes training optimally?

My own, admittedly unscientific, view is that all three are probable reasons for the decline in performance, at least over longer distances. I don't know about sprints like the 100 meters. You only have to look at the age spread by decade in the results of distance races to see, after the age of fifty, the numbers entering decline significantly with every decade that passes. This tells me that people stop running, or at least stop participating in races, as they get older. Is it because of illness or injury? I meet people all the time who tell me they used to run but can no longer run free of discomfort, so chronic injuries may be a factor for some. Others simply become tired of racing and the increasing effort required to train as we age, and they continue to run but stop racing, or move on to other pursuits.

From my observations, it is not only middle-of-the-pack runners who quit as they become older. A good percentage of elite athletes do as well. I have met former elite runners and have been staggered that they quit when they tell me the times they used to run. Reasons I have heard range from loss of the speed they once possessed to loss of interest to the development of chronic injuries. With a smaller pool of athletes participating as the decades go by, one can expect records to be affected. There is simply less competition.

Here is a table of finishers in a popular half-marathon I ran in late 2019,[38] shortly before the pandemic, grouped by age and gender:

Age Group	Men	Women	Total
Under 30	63	103	166
30–39	131	139	270
40–49	116	125	241
50–59	61	40	101
60–69	15	9	24
Over 70	3	1	4
	389	417	806

For both men and women, the numbers were much the same for runners in their thirties and forties, and both are higher than the number of finishers under thirty. After fifty, however, the number of finishers falls dramatically with each passing decade. For me to finish first in the seventy-plus age-group was satisfying, but I only had two competitors to beat! The only woman in the race over seventy won her age-group without any competition. In most of the races I do locally these days, there are no more than five male runners over seventy, at best. I should note this half-marathon was a local race near my home in Connecticut, roughly an hour from New York City, in an area where, interestingly, there are lots of baby boomers and Generation Xers, but not as many people under forty as would be the case in a city like New York. Even so, 84 percent of the finishers were under fifty. These results, and others I have reviewed, illustrate how race participation drops off once people reach fifty.

What is perhaps most interesting about the statistics for this race, however, is that there were more women than men. With every passing year, I see a higher percentage of women at races I run. The era when road racing was primarily a male sport has long passed.

The authors' second theory is a reduction in the time and intensity of training as we age; we simply do not train as hard as we used to when we were younger. If I consider myself and older runners whom I know, this is undoubtedly the case. Is waning enthusiasm to train a factor? Perhaps. I know I do not get to the track and do speed work with the regularity I once did, so my intensity has dropped. On the roads and trails, I run slower and therefore take longer to complete my regular training routes than I used to. Even if I might spend as much time running as I once did on a given day, I am not running as far. For the 10,000 meters and longer distances, long training runs are necessary to optimize performance.

Here is a table of the average distance per year I have run each decade since I turned 30:

Age Group	Miles per Year	Kilometers per Year
30–39	2,140	3,425
40–49	1,316	2,104
50–59	1,468	2,349
60–69	1,333	2,172
From 70	833	1,332

I ran about 50 percent further in my thirties than I did in the decades that followed. This is largely because I was competing regularly in the Comrades Marathon in South Africa in my thirties, and preparing for a race of this distance requires months of getting up before dawn for long training runs. In my forties, fifties, and sixties, the average distance run per year did not vary that much, and I do not believe the intensity changed much either. I continued to do speed work on the track. At least in my case, therefore, the deterioration in my times from my forties to my sixties does not appear to be caused by a reduction in the time and intensity of training.

However, in the six years and counting since I turned seventy, the distances I run, as well as the intensity of my training, has dropped dramatically; I would speculate a part of the reason for the deterioration in my times after turning seventy is, in fact, caused by this factor.

I am not entirely sure why I train less these days, though I would note that I still easily exceed the physical activity guidelines of the WHO outlined in chapter 2. For two years, 2020 and 2021, I believe the pandemic had an impact—the reduced number of races curbed my motivation to put in long runs. It is not due to injury, as I remain injury-free. Is it also because of waning enthusiasm after running and racing for more than four decades? Perhaps. I have little doubt, however, that Lazarus and Harridge's third factor, *"fading integrative physiological capacity,"* is a significant reason. Training undoubtedly becomes harder as one ages. I started to notice this in my early fifties, and the effort required to train accelerates with each passing decade. Make no mistake, I still immeasurably enjoy running, but running is not effortless the way it once was. It takes me longer to warm up and get into my stride. It takes me longer to run a given route than it once did. Let's explore why.

Much research has been carried out and much written about the impact of aging on the human body. In some respects, there is a not a consensus yet on the causes of decline in athletic performance due to physiological factors. No doubt there is much we will learn in the decades to come. There is, however, general acceptance that the loss of aerobic capacity, as measured by VO_2 max, is a significant factor. Studies have shown the gradual loss of aerobic capacity through adult life among athletes is greatly reduced compared to people who are not active; nevertheless, it will gradually decline. Although some studies have shown people in later life who have not been physically active can actually increase their VO_2 max by becoming physically active, that improvement will be followed by the gradual decline in aerobic capacity that seems unavoidable as one ages.

Other factors are reduced muscle strength and reduced flexibility. The best way to mitigate the loss of muscle mass is to do strength training two or three times a week, ideally on nonconsecutive days. I really believe strength training of the leg muscles can make a difference to distance-running performance as one ages; however, it is important to subject all major muscle groups in the body to strength training. Whether one uses bands, equipment in a gym, or free weights is not something on which I will offer advice; suffice to say, it is best to start a strength training program under the guidance of a qualified instructor who can design a personal program for you.

I have never been particularly flexible, even as a child, and therefore introduced a stretching routine early in my running career that I have followed ever since. I discussed the importance of stretching as a measure to reduce the risk of injury in chapter 7. I admit I have gone for long periods when I did not stretch as often as I believe I should, which is several times a week if not every day. Stretching simply becomes more important than ever as one ages to reduce the rate at which we lose flexibility and our range of motion.

Other factors that may come into play are increases in body fat and a reduced capacity to process the buildup of lactic acid in muscles as one exercises.

While it seems to me all three factors mentioned by Lazarus and Harridge in their paper contribute to the decline in athletic performance as one ages, should one be concerned about it? As I discuss in other chapters, the health benefits of running as one ages are immense, and one can obtain much enjoyment from the activity into old age, whether it is socializing with other runners or simply being outdoors alone and close to nature.

One does not need to enter races or aspire to be competitive to enjoy these benefits. For someone like me, however, who has something of a competitive streak but never won anything—in even the most low-key of races—until I turned fifty, the regular winning of age-group prizes after I turned sixty has been rewarding and keeps my interest level up. The year I turned sixty, I trained hard, knowing that age-group awards are almost always in ten-year categories, so one's best chance of winning is in the first year or two after entering a new decade. That year, I won the 60–69 division in the first eight races I entered, ranging in distance from 10k to 50k.

Then when I turned seventy, once again, I put more effort into my training than I had for several years, with a view to compete for age-group prizes at local races after several years of no longer being competitive in the sixty plus category. Over a six-month period, I ran five trail races and thirteen road races, ranging in distance from 5k to 50k and finished first over seventy in all but one, a big 20k race where I was second to a runner from out of state. How long will I keep on entering races? Who knows? But I can see good reasons to continue to compete. First of all, I love the racing scene. Also, as prominent distance runner and author of seven books on running Roger Robinson wrote in an article entitled "Why I Still Love Racing at Age 82," "These days I can break a record while finishing last."[39]

I continue to add to my trophy cabinet into my mid-seventies, but, more importantly, I enjoy running as much as I did when I started out doing a daily run in South Africa all those years ago.

CHAPTER 14

South Africa's Journey to Democracy
(through the Eyes of a Runner)

A ll but the first two years of my schooling in Johannesburg, where I grew up, was at a private all-boys school. I did not think about it at the time, but this was a very sheltered upbringing that did not expose me to the diversity of the South African population, let alone its inequalities. Back then private schools in South Africa were all English language and all white, which meant I was not exposed to the nearly 60 percent of the white population who did not speak English at home, let alone people of other races who made up a majority of the total population. All the teachers were white, and in the upper school, all were male. I ran track and cross-country and played team sports against other schools; these contests were with all-white schools, many of them private, all-boys schools like mine.

From there, I went on to the University of the Witwatersrand, also in Johannesburg, to study to become a professional accountant. This university, founded in 1922 and known colloquially as "Wits" was, and still is, one of the premier institutions of higher learning and research on the African continent. I was not an active runner during my years at Wits, only jogging occasionally on the sports fields to keep in shape for weekend tennis and golf. In the 1960s, when I was there, university education was segregated; there were a few black students but not many, and I never came across any black faculty members. Following segregation of universities in the late 1950s, much to the dismay of institutions like Wits, black students were technically only allowed to register if their chosen course of

study was not available at an institution established for them, such
as Fort Hare, where Nelson Mandela had studied law in the early
1940s—before being accepted at Wits some years later after moving
to Johannesburg.

Even the first few weeks at Wits started to open my eyes to the
injustices of South African society. For the first two semesters, I took
courses in English literature. Unlike my private school teachers, who
never talked about anything political, several of the faculty in the
English department were determined to expose their freshmen students to the realities of South African society through the books they
assigned us and the way they dissected them in class. One lecturer I
remember well was John Paton, son of the prominent South African
author of *Cry the Beloved Country* fame, Alan Paton. Alan had also
been the leader of the Liberal Party, a minor political party with the
then radical platform of one-person, one-vote, regardless of race.

What startled me even more was the stance taken by student
leaders in opposition to the segregation of the universities, as well
as the broader apartheid laws, and the extent of their support among
the student body. I never became involved in student leadership but
admired those who did, some of whom were arrested from time to
time for crossing what was then considered a red line with the views
they advocated. The National Union of South African Students
(NUSAS) was a powerful body that represented the students at the
various white English-language universities and was a constant thorn
in the side of the apartheid government.

In early 1966, NUSAS invited Senator Robert Kennedy to come
to South Africa to deliver its annual Day of Affirmation speech, to
take place that year at the University of Cape Town. The South African government did not want the senator to come but was fearful
of the consequences of not granting him a visa, so they did so on the
understanding that no government officials would meet him. Kennedy made the trip and delivered a powerful speech, one that some
consider his best, to thousands of students in Cape Town in June

1966, two years to the day before his assassination. The president of NUSAS, who had invited Kennedy, was not in the auditorium for the speech, as the government had banned him from attending public gatherings for five years in advance of Kennedy's visit. I only read the speech much later; at the time, South Africa had no television service, and radio stations were government controlled, so it was not broadcast. An extract from the speech, which became known as the "Ripple of Hope" speech, is inscribed on Kennedy's tombstone in Arlington National Cemetery. Kennedy visited four universities, including Wits, in a whirlwind three-day trip. I was one of thousands in attendance for his Wits speech, which contained a similar message of hope to the one delivered in Cape Town.

Robert Kennedy's visit was a kind of an awakening for me as a student at a segregated university; the banning and arrests of student leaders continued, but, to me, the injustices of the system were being exposed more and more. I began to believe that change would come but did not know how or when.

From 1971 to 1973, I was away from South Africa, living and working in Detroit as a young professional accountant. When I returned, I sensed there had been some movement, not with the government, but in the more optimistic mindset of the people with whom I associated, most of whom, at that time, where white. This brings me to my first road race in July 1974, a 24k organized by Wits University's Athletic Club, held at a large open property the university owned about forty-five minutes to the north of the main campus. Several black runners were present at the start. As this was my first race, I did not know what was normal, but experienced runners were saying they had never participated in a multiracial event! The official explanation given was that the black runners were not actually entrants but were using the opportunity to pace other runners as part of their training for some upcoming blacks-only national road race championship.

If the official results for this event still exist somewhere, I imagine they say a well-known local white runner, Dennis Morrison, won the race. My running diary, however, reflects that a black runner named Vincent Rakabaele won the race. At the prize-giving, the winner's trophy was presented to Dennis, who handed it to Vincent; though he was not an official entrant in the event, Vincent had crossed the finish line first. This was a small, but bold, step by the Wits University Athletic Club to push for integration in the sport of road running.

The impact was relatively swift. Ten months later, in May 1975, Vincent Rakabaele was one of a small number of Black athletes at the start of South Africa's most famous road race, the Comrades Marathon, which I described in chapter 12, this time as an official participant. Apartheid in the sport of road running had basically ended, a tiny step on South Africa's journey to democracy over the next two decades. Rakabaele came nineteenth, the first black finisher. He was nineteenth again the following year and fourth in 1977.[40] In the second half of the 1970s, he won many road races that historically had been reserved for whites only. He was a native of Lesotho, a tiny landlocked country within South Africa's borders, and competed in the marathon at the 1980 and 1984 Olympic Games.[41] South Africa was barred from the Olympic Games from 1964 to 1988 because of apartheid, but Rakabaele, while a resident of South Africa, was a citizen of Lesotho, and represented his country of birth at the games.

At the time that white and black runners started to compete together, Rakabaele and several other leading black runners in the Johannesburg area were members of a blacks-only running club affiliated with a local gold mine. Running clubs were, and still are, at the heart of the sport in South Africa; to compete in athletic events, whether on the road, off the road, or on the track, one is required to be a member of a registered club. Clubs were not integrated, and it was unclear whether the authorities would allow the integration of clubs. In advance of entering that first race in July 1974, I had joined Rand Athletic Club (RAC), a club that had been formed two years earlier by three experienced white long-distance runners and that, over the years that followed, became one of the largest and most successful running clubs in the country.

By 1976, I was the club secretary and a member of the club board. One of the members, white of course, approached me about a young black man he knew in the area who loved to run and showed much promise. His name was Hoseah Tjale. We did not investigate the legalities or consult with the sport's governing body; we simply made a decision to admit Hoseah as our first black member and encouraged him to follow his passion. As best we could tell, no other club in the province had made a move toward becoming multiracial before RAC did. There was, in fact, no backlash, so other clubs followed. I remember the first race at which Hoseah made an appearance in our club colors, a 16k road race. He did remarkably well, and we knew he was talented. Early in his career he sometimes joined the group I trained with on weekends, but soon became way too good to run with us. In the months and years that followed, the club continued to admit black members, many of whom were very good runners.

Hoseah became a star for RAC and later joined another running club, where his success continued; he was a force on the local running scene for about fifteen years. Among his many successes, in 1980, he won the prestigious Two Oceans ultramarathon, which I mentioned in chapter 11, as well as the London to Brighton ultramarathon in England in 1985.[42] He was a top competitor in the Comrades Marathon throughout the 1980s and into the early 1990s, including two second- and two third-place finishes.[43]

In the early 1980s, American companies operating in South Africa were under pressure to explain to shareholders and activists why they did not pack up and leave. I wrote to a number of them in my capacity as an officer of RAC to ask for their financial support to send our leading black athletes, none of whom had well-paying jobs, to compete in major events in other parts of the country, such as the Two Oceans. I explained we were a small club not expecting to change the world, but we wanted to play a minor part in helping with the integration of our sport by enabling our athletes with modest financial means to travel to major events. The support we received exceeded my expectations.

By the time I moved back to the United States in 1988, the sport of road running was well and truly integrated, and black athletes were dominant among male runners and gradually becoming so among women. On the political scene, it would be another two years before F. W. De Klerk came to power and freed Nelson Mandala, lifted the ban on the African National Congress and other political organizations, and started to dismantle the various laws that entrenched apartheid, paving the way for the first democratic elections and transfer of the presidency to Mandela. In the late 1970s and 1980s, however, at least in parts of the country like Johannesburg, where I lived, society moved on despite the government, as illustrated by the evolution of our sport. Formerly all-white offices in downtown Johannesburg had become integrated, at least to a degree, some restaurants were accepting customers of all races, and blacks were starting to live openly in formerly all-white suburbs and socialize with white neighbors. It was only a matter of time.

CHAPTER 15

Why Do We Run? Conclusions

The World Health Organization and national health services in many countries recommend at least 150 minutes of "moderate-intensity aerobic physical activity" per week for adults. At least one five-year study, however, suggests that significant health benefits can be derived from regular exercise for less than 150 minutes per week, while numerous studies have confirmed the benefits of regular exercise into old age.

Many forms of aerobic exercise that elevate the heart rate for a sustained period are effective; it does not have to be running. An advantage of running is that one does not need a facility (such as a gym or a squash court), any equipment other than running clothing and shoes, or a partner. Running is something one can do just about anywhere and anytime.

Regular exercise (along with a healthy diet) is a cornerstone for living a healthier life—a longer health span—as well as potentially a longer life span. Studies discussed in chapter 3 have confirmed the benefits of regular exercise in both preventing and managing various chronic conditions, including cardiovascular disease, type 2 diabetes, and certain cancers. Further good news is that studies on the impact of exercise on the aging process have reached two important conclusions:

- It is never too late to start a regular exercise program.
- Any amount of *regular* exercise is better than nothing.

In chapter 4 we looked into the psychological benefits of running, such as managing stress, getting a good night's sleep, and enhancing our determination to succeed and our level of self-confidence.

As I explain in chapter 5, it is important to recognize there can be health risks with running and other forms of exercise, but in most cases, these can be managed. If one is planning to embark on a program of regular exercise that will raise the heart rate, it is a good idea to consult a physician and have a comprehensive physical examination before doing so. The older one is, the more critical it is to do this. If you exercise regularly, I recommend having a physical examination from time to time even if you feel well—you never know what you might find out unexpectedly, as I did, and then you can address the problem.

I strongly suggest you do not run if you have any symptoms of the flu, as this can be dangerous for your health. I do not run if I have the common cold either; I am not likely to improve my fitness level while fighting a virus, and I find going outside for a walk more enjoyable. In time, we will know more about the impact of exercising while having mild symptoms of COVID-19; in the meantime, common sense would suggest avoiding exercise until the symptoms have passed, and one has a negative test.

For people who wish to lose weight, studies are inconclusive as to whether exercise alone can help one to do so. It seems some people can lose weight that way, and others cannot, probably for genetic reasons. There is stronger evidence, however, that physical activity plays a key role in preventing weight gain, including in individuals who have purposefully lost weight through changes to their diet.

We looked into safety considerations in chapter 6. Running is safer than many other sports, but there are still risks. It is important to focus on what you are doing, and on your surroundings, and to avoid being distracted. Parks are a relatively safe place to run, as there are no cars, and the surface may be softer than a paved road or sidewalk. The same is true of running tracks. When running in a park at night, stick to well-lit areas where there are other people around. When running on roads, it is important to follow traffic rules that apply to pedestrians and to use common sense. When possible, run on a sidewalk or a verge and not on the roadway itself. As a rule, run facing oncoming traffic. Always wear brightly colored clothing to be more easily visible to other road users and wear reflective gear if you must run at night. Running on trails can be fun, but one needs to concentrate to avoid tripping over roots and rocks. On remote trails, it is safer to not run alone. If someone is bothering me while I am running, whether on a trail, in a park or on the roads, I have found it best to ignore the person and simply carry on running, and to not engage with the person. This also seems to be the best tactic with dogs that are not under the control of a dog walker.

Long-distance running is a sport where injuries from quick acceleration or changes in direction are rare. Most injuries, as discussed in chapter 7, are a consequence of running distances to which the body has not yet adapted. This is often the case during the first year one takes up running, regardless of age. Fortunately, many injuries do not require complete rest and will heal with a reduction in the distance one runs, or the intensity, or both. A temporary orthotic or brace of some kind may also be helpful, depending on the injury.

There does not seem to be any conclusive evidence that if you start out running with healthy knees, the activity will cause you to develop osteoarthritis of the knees. However, if your knees are not healthy, consult with a specialist before starting a regular running program.

Chapter 8 is about footwear and other running gear. Injuries can also result from running in inappropriate shoes: either the shoes are not suitable for one's build or running style, they are new and inflexible, or they are too worn. It is a good idea to consult a running shoe specialist when starting to run regularly—someone who can analyze the way you run and recommend shoes that suit you. In my experience, a new pair of shoes should ideally be "worn in" before running longer distances in them. As the only equipment a runner needs that is relatively expensive, it is worth replacing shoes before they are worn to the point they may lead to injury.

I like to alternate two pairs of running shoes at different points in their life cycle every few days, so I am not faced with having to switch from a worn-out pair to a new pair overnight and can gradually "wear in" a new pair by alternating them with a pair I have been using for some time. If you want to run on trails, it is worth investing in a pair of trail shoes with treads designed for loose surfaces.

Clothing made from synthetic fibers breathes better than clothing made from natural fibers but is less environmentally friendly. I run in synthetic tops and shorts for comfort but add a second layer, generally made from cotton, when the weather turns cold. If it is very cold, I simply wear a third layer rather than running in a winter jacket, which I personally do not find comfortable. If you want to run on very windy days, however, you need a windbreaker suitable for running.

In colder climates, hats, gloves, and tights or running pants are also an essential part of the runner's wardrobe. Beyond that, the one essential item of equipment needed before one steps outside is some form of identification to wear.

As one ages, one will inevitably run slower. An analysis of age-group track world records for 100 meters and 10,000 meters referred to in chapter 13 shows that there is a roughly linear decline in performance over both distances for men and women until the early to mid-seventies, after which the decline accelerates rapidly. The decline can be attributed to factors such as a drop in the number of competitors as one ages, a reduction in the intensity and time put into training as one ages, and, perhaps most of all, declining physiological capacity.

In my view, this does not matter. I run slower than when I was younger but enjoy running as much as I ever did. I also enjoy the benefits of the fitness that comes with a program of regular exercise well into my seventies. If you continue to enter races, as I do, and set a goal of trying to beat, say, only those who are older than you, there need be no end to your racing career.

Participating in races certainly does not have to be part of a running regimen, but if a novice runner wants to take part in races, whether to compete or just for the fun of it, as I mention in chapter 9, the 5k distance is the place to start after one is into a regular routine of running a few times a week. One does not need months of training to jog a 5k course. There are thousands of 5k races every year, all around the world, as evidence of their popularity. If you want to run longer races, you can step up to the 10k after you run a few 5k races and can manage that distance comfortably. Needless to say, more training is required for a race of double the distance, but most runners who enjoy running a 5k can progress to a 10k and enjoy it as well.

It is, however, a big leap from there to the popular half-marathon, which is 21.1 kilometers or 13.1 miles. Yes, there are 15k and 10-mile races that bridge the gap to the half-marathon, but there are fewer of them. The point is many runners who take part in 5k and 10k races do not run half-marathons or aspire to do so. Fields are larger with the shorter-distance races, and one can enjoy the fun of race day, as well as the health benefits of running, without having to put in all the training required to comfortably run a half-marathon—unless one wants to run longer distances, as some runners do.

What if one has the ambition to run a marathon, 42.2 kilometers or 26.2 miles, the classic road race I talk about in chapter 10, which dates back to the first modern Olympic Games in Athens in 1896? Races of distances between the half-marathon and marathon, such as 30k or 20 miles, are harder to find, but it is worth trying to if one wants to map out a training program to prepare for running a marathon. Training for a marathon properly takes months, yet the popularity of marathons, especially the big city marathons, continues to grow. The most popular city marathons, like Boston, London, Berlin, and New York, have tens of thousands of participants who start in waves at staggered times, but they still turn away thousands who would like to enter but cannot be accommodated. No other road races of any distance attract the large number of spectators who line the routes of the bigger city marathons, which gives the runner a memorable experience, with crowds cheering every athlete and providing encouragement all the way to the finish line. Some runners enter with the idea of running just one marathon but find themselves coming back to repeat the experience and to try to improve their time.

Running races beyond the marathon distance is largely for devoted ultramarathon runners, those who are up for running 50k, 50 miles, 100k, 100 miles, or even further. As discussed in chapter 11, most of the races of these distances, at least in the Unites States, are on trails rather than roads. Ultra-running is a sport in itself; some of the participants only run on trails. Fields in ultramarathons are generally small, spectators are sparse, and there is a unique level of camaraderie among these runners. Times are inevitably slower, but time is not what anyone—other than the runners themselves—seems to care about; it is the distance of the run that fascinates people. While some ultramarathons, like the Comrades Marathon you read about in chapter 12, have a cutoff time to qualify as a finisher, many do not and you can take as long as you like, within reason, to finish and then talk about the distance you ran, rather than time it took.

There is, however, in my experience, a benefit in running longer distances for those dedicated marathon runners who care about improving their times. These runs can be either in the form of long training runs or official ultramarathons. The extra distance helps build stamina that can do wonders getting one through the latter stages of a marathon feeling good and without losing speed.

In conclusion, let me circle back and repeat once more that running in races, whether a 5k or 50k or something in between, is not necessary to achieve the health benefits of regular exercise. I like the racing scene personally; it is something that has been a part of me since 1974. What is important, as a component of a healthy lifestyle, is moderate-intensity aerobic physical activity a few times a week, be that running or some other activity. My hope is to inspire you to be active, remain active, and enjoy life to the fullest, even into old age. I wish you the best of luck.

Selected Achievements as a Runner Over Sixty

Age 60 to 69
2007 Boston Buildup Winter Series—Division winner
2007 USATF Connecticut Road Championships—Member of division winning team
2008 Boston Buildup Winter Series—Division winner
2008 USATF Connecticut Road Championships—Member of division winning team
2014 Norwalk Summer Series—Division winner

Age 70 upward
2017 Norwalk Summer Series—Division winner
2017 Trailmix Series—Division winner
2018 Trailmix Series—Division winner
2019 Westport Summer Series—Division winner
2020 Westport Summer Series (Virtual)—Division winner
2021 Norwalk Summer Series—Division winner
2022 Westport Summer Series—Division winner

Notes:
The USATF Connecticut Road Championships (also known as Connecticut Road Racing Grand Prix Series) is a series of road races across the state with distances from 5k to 20k
The Trailmix Series is a series of races on trails with distances from 8k to half-marathon, mainly in Westchester County, New York.
All the other series are on the road in Fairfield County, Connecticut, with distances up to 25k.

Acknowledgments

M y thanks to all who have helped make running a part of my life since 1974, including:

James and John, who got me started;

Fritz, Caspar, Ray, Ole, Andrew, and the other early leaders of Rand Athletic Club, the club where I enjoyed so much fun in my first fifteen years as a runner;

Gavin and the 1970's Saturday morning group of RAC members;

Dick and Vreni, who took the club to heights I never imagined and continue to do so;

Len, who coached me early on and helped me believe in my potential;

Joe, Maurice, Barry, Bill, and the rest of the late 1970's / 1980's Jan Smuts running group;

Bill and Frank, my main running mates in Luxembourg in the 1990s;

The folks at Serpentine Running Club in London around the time of the millennium, especially Malcolm, captain of our senior men's teams, who got me back into running track and cross-country;

Jim, Marty, Don, and Laddie, without whom there would be no races to run in Fairfield County, Connecticut; as well as all the regulars on the local race scene whom I have gotten to know over the past twenty years.

And my thanks to the team at Palmetto Publishing, with whom it has been such a pleasure to work on this project.

Notes

Chapter 1

1. *Official 2013 Boston Marathon Racers Record Book.*

2. Paul Riefberg, "Getting Old Marathon Results Was a Roller-coaster," accessed May 21, 2021, www.running.net.

Chapter 2

3. Based on an analysis of a DNA sample submitted to 23andMe, 23andme.com

4. Malcolm Gladwell, *Outliers—The Secret of Success* (New York: Little, Brown and Company, 2008), Page 35

5. https://www.who.int/news-room/fact-sheets/detail/physical-activity

6. Mandy Oaklander, "Running Can Help You Live Longer. And More Isn't Always Better," *Time* (US edition), November 18, 2019.

Chapter 3

7. John Taddei, "In the Long Run, Older Runners Live Longer, 21 Year Study Finds," Bloomberg.com, August 11, 2008.

8. Stephen Harridge and Norman Lazarus, "Can Exercise Reverse the Ageing Process," *BBC*, March 20, 2019. Stephen Harridge is a professor of human and applied physiology at King's College London and Norman Lazarus is an emeritus professor at King's College London and a master cyclist in his eighties.

9. Debra L. Blackwell, and Tainya C. Clarke, "State Variation in Meeting the 2008 Federal Guidelines for Both Aerobic and Muscle-Strengthening Activities through Leisure-Time Physical Activity among Adults Aged 18–64: United States, 2010–2015," *National Institutes of Health*, June 28, 2018.

10. Alexander Mok, Kay-Tee Khaw, Robert Luben, Nick Wareham, and Soren Brage, "Physical Activity Trajectories and Mortality: Population Based Cohort Study," *BMJ*, June 26, 2019.

11. Mok, et al., "Physical Activity Trajectories."

12. Pedro F. Saint-Maurice, Diarmuid Coughlan, Scott P. Kelly, Sarah K Keadle, Michael B Cook, Susan A Carlson, Janet E, Fulton Carles E. Matthews, "Association of Leisure-Time Physical Activity across the Adult Life Course with All-Cause and Cause-Specific Mortality," *JAMA* Network Open, March 8, 2019.

13. B. K. Pedersen and B. Saltin, "Exercise as Medicine—Evidence for Prescribing Exercise as Therapy in 26 Different Chronic Diseases," *Scandinavian Journal of Medicine and Science in Sport*, November 25, 2015.

14. Michelle Roberts, "Running Marathon Cuts Years off 'Artery Age,'" *BBC*, January 7, 2020.

15. John J. Ratley and James E. Loehor, "The Positive Impact of Physical Activity on Cognition during Adulthood: A Review of Underlying Mechanisms, Evidence and Recommendations," *Walter de Gruyter, Berlin, New York*, April 2011.

16. Michael Babyak, James A. Blumenthal, Steve Herman, Parinda Khatri, Murali Doraiswamy, Kathleen Moore, Edward W. Craighead, Teri T. Baldewicz and Krishnan K Ranga "Exercise Treatment for Major Depression: Maintenance of Therapeutic Benefit at 10 Months," *Psychosomatic Medicine*, September 2000.

Chapter 4

17. Mark Wexler, "Many Songs Lifting Spirits," National Wildlife, Winter 2023: page 12

18. Freya Oswald, Jennifer Campbell, Chloë Williamson, Justin Richards, Paul Kelly, "A Scoping Review of the Relationship between Running and Mental Health," *International Journal of Environmental Research and Public Health*, November 1, 2020.

Chapter 5

19. "Jim Fixx," Wikipedia, accessed September 1, 2022. (In the case of references to articles posted on Wikipedia.com, the title of the article at the date it was accessed is provided; as Wikipedia is constantly updated, URLs are not provided.)

20. Sanghamitra Mohanty, Prasant Mohanty, Megumi Tamaki, Veronica Natale, Carola Gianni, Chintan Trivedi, Yalcin Gokoglan, Luigi di Biase, Andrea Natale, "Differential Association of Exercise Intensity with Risk of Atrial Fibrillation in Men and Women: Evidence from a Meta-Analysis," *Journal of Cardiovascular Electrophysiology*, June 2016.

21. B. Jug, M. Sebestjen, M. Sabovic, M. Pohar, and I. Keber, "Atrial Fibrillation is an Independent Determinant of Increased NT-proBNP Levels in Outpatients with Signs and Symptoms of Heart Failure," pubmed.gov, 2009.25

Chapter 6

22. "The Central Park Jogger Case," Wikipedia, accessed October 8, 2022

Chapter 7

23. James L. Fixx, *The Complete Book of Running* (London, Chatto and Windus, 1979). Page 168

24. T. D. Noakes, *Lore of Running* (Cape Town, Oxford University Press, 1985). Page 325

25. T. D. Noakes, *Lore of Running* (Cape Town, Oxford University Press, 1985). Page 335

26. Rand Athletic Club, Johannesburg, newsletter for members, Winter 2021.

Chapter 8

27. Christopher McDougall, *Born to Run: A Hidden Tribe, Superathletes, and the Greatest Race the World Has Never Seen* (New York, Vintage Books, 2009). Page 168

Chapter 9

28. Worldathletics.org. accessed September 8, 2021

Chapter 10

29. "Marathon," Wikipedia, accessed October 10, 2021

30. "Patriots' Day," Wikipedia, accessed October 18, 2022

Chapter 11

31. Bbc.co.uk, accessed June 14, 2019, Catra 54, California, *I was addicted to drugs, now I am addicted to running*

32. twooceansmarathon.org. accessed October 31, 2021

Chapter 12

33. Comrades.com, accessed October 31, 2021. All the information that follows in Chapter 12 on the growth in the number of entrants and finishers is from this source, which is the official race website.

34. Comrades.com, accessed October 31, 2021

35. "Wally Hayward," Wikipedia, accessed October 31, 2021

Chapter 13

36. "Blue Zone," Wikipedia, accessed October 24, 2022

37. Normal R. Lazarus and Stephen D. R. Harridge, "Declining Performance of Master Athletes: Silhouettes of the Trajectory of Healthy Human Ageing?" *Journal of Physiology* (November 2, 2016).

38. Official results of the 2019 SONO Half Marathon, Norwalk. Connecticut on October 6, 2019

39. Roger Robinson, "Why I Still Love Racing at Age 82," *Outside*, December 21, 2021, https://www.outsideonline.com/health/running/racing-after-80-aging-inspiration-senior-fitness/.

Chapter 14

40. Comrades.com, accessed October 31, 2021

41. "Vincent Rakabaele," Wikipedia, accessed October 31, 2021

42. "Hoseah Tjale," Wikipedia, accessed October 31, 2021

43. Comrades.com, accessed October 31, 2021

Ingram Content Group UK Ltd.
Milton Keynes UK
UKHW020920190723
425423UK00004B/233